MW00380715

A Guide to Writing Successful Engineering Specifications

David C. Purdy, P. E.
Vice President, Engineering
Applied Power Associates, Inc.

McGraw-Hill, Inc.

New York   St. Louis   San Francisco   Auckland   Bogotá
Caracas   Hamburg   Lisbon   London   Madrid
Mexico   Milan   Montreal   New Delhi   Paris
San Juan   São Paulo   Singapore
Sydney   Tokyo   Toronto

McGraw-Hill Professional & Reference Division offers business audio tapes & CD-ROM products in science and technology. For information & a catalogue, please write to Audio/Optical Media Dept., McGraw-Hill Professional & Reference Dept., 11 West 19th St., NY, NY 10011

Library of Congress Cataloging-in-Publication Data

Purdy, David C.
  A guide to writing successful engineering specifications.

    p. cm.
  Includes index.
    1. Engineering—Specifications.   2. Specification writing.
  I. Title.
  TA180.P87   1991   620—dc20   90-39148
  ISBN 0-07-050999-9

Copyright © 1991 by McGraw-Hill, Inc. All rights reserved. Printed in the United States of America. Except as permitted under the United States Copyright Act of 1976, no part of this publication may be reproduced or distributed in any form or by any means, or stored in a data base or retrieval system, without the prior written permission of the publisher.

1 2 3 4 5 6 7 8 9 0   DOC/DOC   9 6 5 4 3 2 1

ISBN 0-07-050999-9

The sponsoring editor for this book was Robert W. Hauserman, the editing supervisor was Caroline Levine, the designer was Naomi Auerbach, and the production supervisors were Suzanne W. Babeuf and Pamela Pelton. It was set in Baskerville by McGraw-Hill's Professional Publishing composition unit.

For more information about other McGraw-Hill materials, call 1-800-2-MCGRAW in the United States. In other countries, call your nearest McGraw-Hill office.

Contents

Preface

Many people think that engineering is complete when design and analysis are complete. This is not so, since engineering is an applied, not a theoretical, art. It is not complete until a machine or structure is in use. After the design is complete, fabrication or construction must occur, or the project is incomplete.

Modern society is based on specialization of function. Each person, ideally, does what he or she does best and passes the results of that work to the next person in the process. Individuals are grouped into organizations which, in sum and ideally, do what they do best and pass the results of their work to the next organization in the process. One result of this specialization is that communication is a major problem in modern management. Specifications are a form of interorganization communication.

In the construction industries, engineering and architectural companies are usually separate from, and independent of, equipment vendors and construction organizations. In the manufacturing industries, engineering and manufacturing are usually in the same corporation but are separate departments. In either event, the engineering organization communicates its design by specifications and drawings. The drawings are often attachments to, and therefore part of, the specifications. A difference with respect to specifications is that construction industry specifications have to take commercial considerations into account, while manufacturing specifications may not.

In both industries, the final product of an engineering organization is not design and analysis but specifications and drawings. The success of an engineering organization depends on the quality of the specifications and drawings, including the design expressed by them.

The importance of specifications is apparent. It is therefore surprising how difficult it is to find engineers who can prepare them well. Perhaps this is because many engineers are more at home in the world of mathematics and graphics than in the world of words. Such a tendency is certainly reinforced by their education, which is strongly oriented toward analysis rather than explanation. Their education usually does little to prepare them specifically for the task of preparing specifications.

This book is intended to aid engineers in the preparation of specifications. If one follows the rules and hints presented here and supplements them with goal-oriented common sense, he or she should be able to prepare specifications which carry out a design economically and with a minimum of problems.

The focus of the book is on preparation of specifications. A proper specification cannot be prepared, however, without proper regard to the selection of a vendor, use of the information the vendor provides, and enforcement of the specification. All these aspects must be considered when writing the specification if it is to be used for external procurement. Therefore, they are described in the book to the extent necessary for specification preparation.

The book has been developed as a handbook, that is, as a book to be kept at hand and referred to during the work. Each chapter contains practical guidance for executing an aspect of specification preparation. Most chapters are supplemented by a checklist which can be used first to plan an effort and later to ensure that the effort is truly complete.

As much as practical, this book is intended for use by people in all industries. It tries to be independent of the practices in any individual industry. Instead, it presents specification technique common to all industries. Engineers at different positions in the organization hierarchy will also find the book useful. Managers will find the chapters on the process (1 to 6) useful in planning a project effort. Engineers on the working level will find the chapters on techniques (7 to 13) useful in their day-to-day work.

This book is also designed to be used as a text in a college or technical school course. The number of chapters is consistent with a semester length. As much as practical, each chapter has been designed to be suitable for one lecture. If necessary, Chaps. 8 and 9 can be split to provide fifteen lectures.

David C. Purdy

Acknowledgments

I am grateful to many people who have helped me, over the years, to learn about specifications. Some were my supervisors, who told me how they wanted specifications written. Others were fellow workers, who helped me. Others were specification writers, mostly unknown, who provided examples of how to, and how not to, write specifications. An especially effective group were the vendors, who found most of the faults in my specifications after they were issued. Another effective group were salespeople, who often made positive suggestions during specification preparation.

I want to acknowledge specifically the help of the people who reviewed the manuscript, that is, Jay Bacharier, William Golde, Samuel Purdy, Michael Vivirito, and Theodore Young. They all made valuable suggestions and helped produce a much better document than I could have produced by myself. I retain responsibility for the book, since I decided how to use their comments.

John Eichler of Gibbs and Hill, Inc., and Dr. Dayton Wittke of the Omaha Public Power District graciously granted permission to use materials in the book.

PART 1
Processes

1
Getting Organized

General

A *specification* is simply a statement of requirements. In engineering or architecture, a specification is a tool for obtaining equipment, goods, or services in accordance with an engineer's or architect's requirements.

Specifications can be divided into two classes—administrative and procurement. *Administrative* specifications are used within an organization. Their function is to tell one branch of an organization what is required by another branch or to provide a record of the criteria used to develop a product. Since they are internal, commercial requirements are not stated to the extent that they would be for a procurement specification. Commercial factors such as price or cost are important in all engineering and architecture work. In an administrative specification, however, one need not be as concerned with the possibility of a substandard, low-cost product as a response to a specification, since the pressure to meet competition is not present. Therefore, some matters which would have to be explicitly stated in a procurement specification can be left unsaid.

A *procurement* specification becomes part of a contract or purchase order. The complete document sent to a bidder can be termed a procurement document. It comprises a technical specification and a commercial section. The two parts must be coordinated. The coordination, plus the need to avoid substandard goods, makes the procurement specification a more demanding document than the administrative specification. This book will focus on procurement specifications, since most of the requirements are the same and since the ability to write procurement specifications encompasses the ability to write administrative specifications.

Today's competitive climate predominantly requires that engineering

3

and architectural work be performed more efficiently than has been
necessary in the past. Work is often performed on a fixed-price basis
rather than on the cost-plus basis often used in the recent past. This
practice requires great care in planning engineering and architectural
work and estimating its cost. Too low an initial estimate results in a loss
of money, while too high an estimate results in a loss of jobs. Good planning from the beginning is therefore a necessity. Even if one does perform work on a cost-plus basis, one must usually establish some credi-
bility as an efficient producer to meet the competition.

The following discussion will treat the specification effort in isolation.
This is an arbitrary convention, necessary to limit the scope of the book.
Actually, it will be realized that planning and executing the specification
effort is closely intertwined with the rest of the effort. Some organizations have an independent specification department, rendering separation of the specification effort necessary. Most organizations do the
specifications in the engineering or architectural department, making
the specification work inseparable.

A specification writing effort is generally part of a larger activity. For
the purpose of describing the process of getting organized, it will initially be assumed that the larger effort is construction of a facility such
as a chemical processing plant or a power plant. The emphasis in this
type of project is on the process that is carried on in the project. This
type of project can be termed an *equipment-oriented project*. Other types
of projects will be considered in subsequent examples.

To start the specification effort, it will be further assumed that the
project has been defined to the point where the scope is known, an
overall schedule has been established, and budgets—construction and
engineering—exist.

Before the specification effort can be planned, a plan for conducting
the project must exist. In general, when an owner decides to acquire an
equipment-oriented project, the services of an engineering group will
be obtained first, either by using the company's own internal group or
by contracting with an engineering firm. This group or firm is usually
referred to collectively as the *engineer*. The actual construction is performed by another set of groups called *constructors*. The term constructor describes a firm's function. Unfortunately, constructors are also
called *contractors*. This term is confusing, since contracts are used to define the role of many parties, including vendors. The constructors are
generally organizations hired by the owner for one particular project
since the owner rarely has the resources to perform the construction
with company personnel. There may be several construction firms on a

large project. Some of the construction firms may be subcontractors, under contract to another constructor. There is generally at least a civil, mechanical, and an electrical constructor. Equipment can be procured either directly by the owner or by the constructors.

The relationships between the owner, the engineer, and the construction contractor(s) must be determined. One approach would be to give the total project to one engineer-constructor. In this case, one omnibus specification covering all aspects of design and construction must be prepared at the beginning of the project. The other extreme is to have the engineer specify and procure the equipment, with several contractors completing various aspects of construction. In this case, the engineer serves as construction coordinator. Then separate specifications have to be prepared for each construction contractor and also must cover all the equipment.

If the assumptions regarding project scope, schedule, and budget are correct, a conceptual design for the project must also exist. This preliminary design would include general arrangement drawings, fluid system flow diagrams, electrical one-line diagrams, and data tabulations. The data tabulations should include an equipment list, instrumentation description, tabulation of architectural and structural materials, and a foundation concept. This information and the project plan will suffice for development of the specification list. It is possible to prepare the specification list without all this data specifically in hand, but the absence of any part of it increases the chance that something will be omitted from the list.

The project plan described above is appropriate for a heavy industry, or equipment-dominated projects. In the building industry, the emphasis is on the building itself, rather than on the equipment inside of it. This industry has developed a more standard set of practices. An architect designs the building and prepares a set of drawings and specifications for it. There is usually one contractor who procures all the structure and equipment for the building. As with the heavy industry project, the preliminary design is the basis for development of the specification list. The dominant feature of the preliminary design influencing the specification list is structural commodities, rather than equipment.

Other industries will have their own appropriate methods for developing a preliminary design and the consequent specification list. The shipbuilding industry, for example, is an industry that is like heavy industry in its emphasis on equipment but is like the building industry in that the nature of the product necessitates one constructor.

Types of Specifications

The simplest kind of specification occurs when a person walks into a hardware store and says something like "Give me a box of ¾ inch, number six, flat head, steel wood screws." Unfortunately, engineering specifications are universally more complex than a simple oral statement. Specifications for complete projects can be several hundred pages and comprise several volumes. Most specifications can be divided into three categories—commodity specifications, catalog specifications, and formal specifications.

Commodity specifications are simple ones, a few sentences at most, which can be sent to one or more vendors on a purchase order or request for quotations form. No technical evaluation is necessary. The purchasing department can merely accept the lowest price. The commodity specification is very good for procuring standard items like small-diameter pipe and fittings since it involves a minimum of effort.

The *catalog* specification simply specifies by citing a manufacturer and model number. In the building industry, such a specification is termed a *proprietary* specification. An example of such a specification, in its entirety, might be "Greenheck model SQB-10-7 fan." Such a specification is more restrictive than a commodity specification but equally simple and effective. An engineer would prepare such a specification after reviewing the features of the fan and its parameters in the manufacturer's catalog and being satisfied that the fan will perform the desired service. Probably, too, the engineer will have experience with the vendor and know that the selection will perform adequately. Price, in this case, is relatively inflexible. It may be the price listed in the catalog, less a standard or customer specific discount. If the product is widely distributed by retailers, such as a popular brand of paint, the price to the consumer may vary depending on which retailer the consumer buys it from. Price inflexibility is not too much of a disadvantage if the goods are inexpensive and if the engineer has considered price in the selection. For a small item, the cost of an engineer's time in preparing a more complete specification and evaluating bids can be greater than the savings in price from the more elaborate procedure.

The *formal* specification is a multisection, usually multipage, document which gives complete technical requirements for goods or services. It is used whenever a commodity specification or a catalog specification will not suffice. Most specifications on heavy industry projects have to be formal specifications. Commodity or catalog specifications are more common in the building industry.

A specification is usually viewed as a document covering one subject and intended for one vendor. Often, a single document called a specification will have several individual sections which fit the above description. A simple case is the specification for a house. It is intended for issue to a general contractor. It will contain a section covering the house's structure, which is provided by the general contractor. It will also contain a plumbing section, intended for a plumbing subcontractor, an electrical section intended for an electrical subcontractor, and possibly other sections intended for other subcontractors. Each of these sections is a specification. We will term such an overall document a *compound specification.*

A specification covering a single subject and intended for a single vendor will be termed a *simple specification.* This term will also be used for a section of a compound specification.

A simple specification can cover more than one piece of equipment, provided that the pieces are similar and one vendor can provide all of them. An example is a specification for centrifugal pumps, which can cover a number of pumps. The text of the specification will cover all the pumps. The parameters of each pump may be given in data sheets which are part of the specification.

Developing the Specification List

The first step in planning an activity is determining its scope. In the case of a specification effort, the best way to define the scope is to develop the specification list, i.e., a list giving the title of each specification on the project. A well-planned specification effort will control production to the level of the individual simple specifications. That is the most convenient level for many purposes, including estimating technical time, scheduling, and assignment of personnel. The specification list should include the individual sections of compound specifications.

Most engineering firms are organized along "discipline" lines. A chemical process firm may have process, piping and equipment, electrical, and structural as major departments. A power plant–oriented company might use mechanical, electrical, and structural as major departments. Architectural and manufacturing firms would use the same organizing principle but different department titles. In any event, a senior engineer in each discipline will develop the specification list for that discipline. The total project list is a synthesis of the departmental lists.

There is no universally recognized procedure for developing a specification list. The discipline engineers draw upon their experience and knowledge of project design to develop the list. Most engineering projects are at least partially repetitious, so past experience is a good guide. Some general guidelines can be applied.

First, the specification list must cover everything required for the project. All construction must be assigned to one of the construction contractors. All equipment on the equipment list must be covered in some specification. Equipment, such as valves and instruments, that is too small and numerous to warrant a place on the equipment list, must be assigned to a specification. Similarly, commodities such as concrete and structural steel, also not found on the equipment list, must be assigned to a specification.

The specification list may contain some specifications which are used as attachments to other specifications and are used to procure equipment furnished as part of a package. One such example is an electric motor specification. Motors are often procured with their driven equipment such as pumps or fans. Another common example is coatings and paint applied to equipment. Coatings and paint used during construction are usually in an independent specification.

Second, the question of grouping equipment into specifications must be addressed. Each major piece of equipment will have its own specification. Smaller equipment can be specified in groups. One specification can cover all centrifugal pumps or all oil-filled transformers. Grouping must be done with judgment and redetermined for each new project. On a large power plant project, boiler feed pumps, condensate pumps, and circulating-water pumps will all have their own specifications, since there are only a small number of manufacturers who can furnish such pumps. On a small project, these pumps can be included with the other centrifugal pumps. Similarly, power output transformers, which are large and require long lead times, are often specified separately from other transformers for large projects but not for small ones.

The specification list should also cover the grouping of specifications into compound specifications. Such grouping will not affect the person-day estimate much, but it will affect scheduling.

To clarify the development of a specification list, consider the example of a small project. It will be the addition of a cooling tower to an existing facility. The cooling tower is a structure standing on its own foundation. Associated with the cooling tower is a small structure (the electrical enclosure) containing a motor control center and a control panel. This project will be titled "Imaginary Project 1." The equipment list for this project is shown in Table 1-1. It, with other aspects of the preliminary design, forms the basis for the specification list. The discipline engineers, after reviewing this list, will realize, based on their experience with previous projects, that the goods shown in Table 1-2 and

Table 1-1. Imaginary Project 1: Equipment List

Item number	Name
M1	Cooling tower
M2	Circulating pump
M3	Makeup pump
M4	Chemical treatment tank
M5	Chemical treatment pump
M6	Electrical enclosure vent fan
M7	Electrical enclosure unit heater
E1	Motor control center
E2	Control panel

Table 1-2. Imaginary Project 1: Commodities List

Mechanical
   Piping and supports
   Valves
Electrical
   Cables
   Conduit
   Instrumentation and control components
Structural
   Concrete
   Structural steel

the services shown in Table 1-3 will also have to be procured in addition to the equipment. They will then develop the specification list shown in Table 1-4. It includes all the equipment, goods, and services required by the lists in Tables 1-1, 1-2, and 1-3. The only combination possible in this simple case was to put both centrifugal pumps, the circulating pump and the makeup pump, in one specification. Also, the chemical treatment pump and tank were procured as a chemical treatment system. This system will include its own instrumentation and control system.

The project plan for Imaginary Project 1 called for one general contractor. It also called for all major equipment to be procured by the

Table 1-3. Imaginary Project 1: Erection Services List

Mechanical
  Equipment installation
  Piping and valves installation
  Start-up and test
Electrical
  Installation
  Start-up and test
Structural
  Concrete placement
  Steel erection
  Excavation and backfilling
  Electrical enclosure and erection

Table 1-4. Imaginary Project 1: Specification List

No.	Title
M1	Cooling tower
M2	Centrifugal pumps
M3	Chemical treatment system
E1	Motor control center
E2	Control panel
S1	Electrical enclosure
CM1	Electrical enclosure vent fan
CM2	Electrical enclosure unit heater
CM3	Piping and supports
CM4	Valves
CM5	Mechanical equipment erection
CM6	Mechanical start-up and test
CE1	Cables and conduit
CE2	Instrumentation and control components
CE3	Electrical installation
CE4	Electrical start-up and test
CS1	Concrete
CS2	Structural steel
CS3	Excavation and backfilling
CS4	Electrical enclosure and erection

owner and all minor components and commodities to be procured by the contractor. Specifications have been grouped accordingly.

The specification list developed as outlined above will be used for developing person-day estimates, for scheduling, and for controlling the project.

It is also good practice to assign an identification number to each specification at this time to keep an orderly account. It will be used for subsequent efforts such as scheduling and person-day control. In many industries, identification numbers can be assigned based on the needs of the project. In the building industry, it will enhance communication if the standard numbering system of the Construction Specification Institute is used.

Preparing the Person-day Estimate

A *person-day* is a unit of work. It is defined as the work that can be reasonably expected to be accomplished by one person working for one day.

The overall project person-day estimate is a vital item, since it is the dominating factor in establishing the price for the project. Too high an estimate results in losing the work. Too low an estimate compared to the performance actually realized later leads to a loss of money. In either case, the organization suffers. The person-day estimate for the specification effort is an important part of the total.

In order to develop a person-day estimate, it is necessary to define the starting point and the endpoint for the activity. The starting point for the specification effort is generally taken to be the commencement of actual writing. The system design, including definition of the type of equipment, number of components, and calculation of design parameters, should be complete before an individual specification is started. The specification writer should not be expected to perform any calculations to supply information for the specification. That is considered to be part of system design. The writer might be expected to determine materials to be applied, based on chemical conditions furnished by the system designer. This is because the writer is expected to be an expert on the equipment being specified and is also expected to know what materials are available and which vendors are accustomed to using them.

For person-day estimating purposes, the endpoint of the specification effort is generally taken to be issuance of the purchase order or contract to the vendor. This means that the specification effort includes writing the specification, answering bidders' questions, writing addenda or modifications that arise therefrom, evaluating the proposals, negotiating with the chosen vendor, and issuing the purchase order or contract. Later activities, such as reviewing vendor drawings, are considered as part of the subsequent engineering and design effort. Inspection is also considered a separate effort.

Preparation of the specification list and the person-day estimate is considered as occurring prior to the start of the specification effort since it is part of planning for the specification.

The specification effort person-day estimate is usually prepared by a senior engineer in each discipline. If an independent specification writing group, independent of the design group, exists, the specification effort is estimated by that group. The engineer preparing the estimate should have extensive experience in specifications. The fundamental procedure is to estimate a number of person-days for each specification. The estimate is very judgmental. It is helpful to have feedback from previous projects which shows results achieved. Failing the availability of feedback, the best guide is past experience in similar situations. If the estimator lacks experience in a particular area, he or she should consult with someone who does. In any event, there should be an estimate for every item on the specification list, even if it is based on poor information. No estimate is automatically an error on the low side. The estimate is dependent on the quality and experience of the engineers later assigned to the project to perform the work, so it is important for the estimator to know the staff. The estimator will modify the basic person-day estimate to suit the quality of available people.

In many cases it will be found that an existing specification, either a standard specification or a specification from a previous project, can be applied to the project at hand with little or no modification. This is the case with minimum person-day requirements. Even in this case, some person-days are required to ensure that advances in technology do not require modifications to the specification and to incorporate client preferences. Also, even with a perfectly applicable specification, some person-days have to be allotted for the development of data sheets for the current project and for the later activities like answering vendor questions and performing the proposal evaluation.

At the other extreme, an entirely new specification might have to be developed, since prior experience with the item being specified does not exist. It may be necessary to perform some research to determine what provisions have to be included in the specification. It may also be necessary to interview vendors to ensure that the specification, when written, will elicit responsive proposals. All this takes time which must be included in the person-day estimate.

For all specifications, time must be included in the estimate for quality-control reviews by engineering supervisors and for interdisciplinary reviews. The latter reviews ensure that the project is properly coordinated.

In the case of Imaginary Project 1, two aids are used in development of the person-day estimate. First, as shown in Table 1-5, the specifications are categorized. Second, as shown in Table 1-6, a development procedure is assigned to each specification. The development procedure includes the drawings that form a part of the specification. Production of the drawings is part of the design, not the specification, effort. The specification writers will need time to review the drawings and ensure that they are suitable for the specification. In the case of this small project, a major part of the effort in using standard specifications

Table 1-5. Imaginary Project 1: Specification Categories

No.	Title	Category
M1	Cooling tower	Formal
M2	Centrifugal pumps	Formal
M3	Chemical treatment system	Formal
E1	Motor control center	Formal
E2	Control panel	Formal
S1	Electrical enclosure	Formal
CM1	Electrical enclosure vent fan	Catalog
CM2	Electrical enclosure unit heater	Catalog
CM3	Piping and supports	Commodity (goods); full (erection)
CM4	Valves	Commodity
CM5	Mechanical equipment erection	Formal
CM6	Mechanical start-up and test	Formal
CE1	Cables and conduit	Commodity
CE2	Instrumentation and control components	Catalog
CE3	Electrical installation	Formal
CE4	Electrical start-up and test	Formal
CS1	Concrete	Formal
CS2	Structural steel	Formal
CS3	Excavation and backfilling	Formal
CS4	Electrical enclosure and erection	Formal

Table 1-6. Imaginary Project 1: Specification Development Procedures

No.	Title	Procedure
M1	Cooling tower	Standard specification; performance tables
M2	Centrifugal pumps	Standard specification; performance tables
M3	Chemical treatment system	New specification
E1	Motor control center	Standard specification; performance tables; arrangement drawing
E2	Control panel	New specification; arrangement drawing
S1	Electrical enclosure	New specification; arrangement drawing
CM1	Electrical enclosure vent fan	Catalog search
CM2	Electrical enclosure unit heater	Catalog search; installation drawing
CM3	Piping and supports	Standard specification; data tabulations; arrangement drawings
CM4	Valves	Data tabulations
CM5	Mechanical equipment erection	New specification
CM6	Mechanical start-up and test	New specification
CE1	Cable and conduit	Data tabulations
CE2	Instrumentation and control components	Data tabulations
CE3	Electrical installation	New specification; interconnection diagrams
CE4	Electrical start-up and test	New specification
CS1	Concrete	Standard specification; arrangement drawing
CS2	Structural steel	Standard specification; arrangement drawing
CS3	Excavation and backfilling	Standard specification; arrangement drawing
CS4	Electrical enclosure and erection	New specification; arrangement drawing

will consist of deleting the parts that do not apply. The resulting person-day estimate is shown in Table 1-7.

The discussion so far has addressed technical requirements and the activities of the engineering department. There are also administrative aspects to be considered, which are developed by the contract and pur-

Table 1-7. Imaginary Project 1: Specification Estimate

No.	Title	Person-days
M1	Cooling tower	1
M2	Centrifugal pumps	1
M3	Chemical treatment system	3
E1	Motor control center	3
E2	Control panel	3
S1	Electrical enclosure	2
CM1	Electrical enclosure vent fan	0.5
CM2	Electrical enclosure unit heater	0.5
CM3	Piping and supports	2
CM4	Valves	1
CM5	Mechanical equipment erection	2
CM6	Mechanical start-up and test	2
CE1	Cable and conduit	0.5
CE2	Instrumentation and control components	2
CE3	Electrical installation	2
CE4	Electrical start-up and test	1
CS1	Concrete	1
CS2	Structural steel	1
CS3	Excavation and backfilling	1
CS4	Electrical enclosure and erection	1
	Total	30.5

chasing departments. Time must be included in the project budget for these functions.

The result of this effort is the number of person-days for each specification and, by summarization, the person-days required for the total specification effort. This product will be used for project cost estimates and for scheduling.

Specification Preparation Schedule

In the introduction to this chapter, it was assumed that a project schedule existed. The specification schedule has to be developed as a part of the overall project schedule. An explicit specification schedule is required at the start of the project to assure that the proper staff and other resources are assembled at the appropriate time.

A total project schedule can be divided into three parts: engineering, procurement, and construction. Each of these portions must respect and support each other. Each must be adjusted to suit the needs of the other. Construction must be adjusted to suit the time when equipment and materials can be made available. Engineering sequence must be adjusted to respect practical construction sequence. The establishment of a detailed project schedule is a process of reconciling the time spans and sequences desired by the various parties and making them into a rational plan. The specification schedule must be fitted to the project schedule.

The initial date requirement for completing a specification is obtained by working backward from the project completion date through equipment delivery date, equipment lead time, proposal preparation time, and proposal evaluation time. Due allowance must be made for administrative and communication time at each stage.

The earliest practical starting time for each specification is established by the development of the necessary engineering information. It is not practical to start writing a specification until equipment parameters and materials requirements are available.

The time span for writing each individual specification derives from the person-day estimate. Since it is usually impractical to assign more than one engineer to write one specification unless it is a compound specification with a number of subsections, the time span for preparation of an individual specification is usually equal to the person-day estimate for it.

Ideally, the time span between the earliest possible start date and the required finish date is longer than the time required to prepare the specification. If not, an adjustment must be made to either the specification schedule or the project schedule.

Another factor to be considered in the development of a specification schedule is the availability of people. This is more of a problem in a small organization than in a large one. It is difficult and painful to decrease and later increase the number of people in an organization. It is also uneconomical to keep people on a force who are not doing useful work. Therefore, every effort is made to keep the number of people in an organization as constant as practical. The specification schedule is adjusted to suit this problem. If necessary, specification engineers are shifted to other work when they are not needed for specifications.

The specification schedule is usually prepared by the scheduling group that does the overall schedule in cooperation with project management and engineering management. Engineering management supplies the time span for preparation of each specification, information on what events must occur before each specification can be started, and information on the availability of personnel to write the specification. The scheduling group uses this information in developing the schedule.

A schedule for Imaginary Project 1 is presented in Table 1-8. Com-

Table 1-8. Imaginary Project 1: Specification Production Schedule

No.	Title	Completion date*
M1	Cooling tower	30
M2	Centrifugal pumps	40
M3	Chemical treatment system	34
E1	Motor control center	30
E2	Control panel	33
S1	Electrical enclosure	40
CM1	Electrical enclosure vent fan	55
CM2	Electrical enclosure unit heater	55
CM3	Piping and supports	57
CM4	Valves	58
CM5	Mechanical equipment erection	53
CM6	Mechanical start-up and test	60
CE1	Cables and conduit	55
CE2	Instrumentation and control components	57
CE3	Electrical installation	59
CE4	Electrical start-up and test	60
CS1	Concrete	57
CS2	Structural steel	58
CS3	Excavation and backfilling	59
CS4	Electrical enclosure and erection	60

*Working days after project initiation.

pletion dates for the major equipment specifications were determined by lead time for the equipment and the requirement that equipment arrive on site when needed by the erector. All the construction specifications will be consolidated into one construction document and issued on the same day. Differences in completion dates are because one specification writer in each major discipline is assumed to be assigned to the project. The writer prepares each subspecification in turn. Completion dates are specified as days after project initiation since this is a planning document, prepared before initiation. Calendar dates can be specified later.

Setting Specification Format Standards

Each project should have a standard format for its specifications. The client has a right to see specifications that look as though they were written by a coherent organization, rather than by a crowd of individual practitioners. Setting the format can be a duty of the project manager, or it might be dictated by company procedures.

The organization of the total procurement document depends on the

Table 1-9. Procurement Document
Organization: Example 1

A. Notice to bidders

B. Instructions to bidders

C. Proposal

D. Agreement

E. Instructions for performance bond

F. General conditions

G. Special conditions

H. Technical requirements

J. Appendices

project's procurement procedure. The total procurement document consists of two major parts—the technical specification and the commercial section. The technical specification covers the technical requirements. The commercial section covers financial, administrative, legal, and contractual matters. The two parts must be in harmony.

One example of a procurement document organization, taken from a governmental organization, is shown in Table 1-9. There is no forwarding letter, since it is intended that notice of the procurement will be placed in a newspaper or other public document such as the *Federal Register*. Anyone can obtain a copy of the procurement document and submit a bid.

Table 1-10 shows a much simpler procurement document organization, used for a private concern.

Since this book is about specifications, the commercial part of the procurement document will not be considered except as it affects the technical specification. The commercial part of a procurement document is very important to the specification writer. The absence of discussion about it is not intended to minimize its importance but to limit the book's scope. Often, the commercial part of the procurement document is prepared by the project's owner, rather than by the engineer. It then follows the owner's standard practice. Owners can be very rigid about modifying their part of the procurement document, so harmonization usually means modifying the specification.

One troublesome section of the procurement document is Instructions to Bidders. This section defines the information the vendor is to submit in response to the procurement document. Since this informa-

Table 1-10. Procurement Document
Organization: Example 2

Forwarding letter
Instructions to bidders
Technical specification
Terms and conditions

tion is the basis for evaluating the proposals, it is very important to the specification engineer.

Table 1-11 shows the table of contents for a typical specification, designed to fit with the procurement document organization shown in Table 1-10. Sections 16, 17, 18, and 20 could have been placed in the commercial part of the procurement document, since they are basically commercial matters. They are also important to the evaluation effort. Placing them in the technical specification gives the specification engineer better control over the information that will be received.

The table of contents need not be identical for every specification on a project. Some flexibility is proper to suit the scope and technical conditions of each specification. The example shown in Table 1-3, for in-

Table 1-11. Typical Specification Table of Contents

Section		Page no.
1.00	Contract terms and conditions	1
2.00	Scope	1
3.00	Equipment to be furnished	2
4.00	Equipment to be furnished by others	5
5.00	Site conditions	6
6.00	Codes and standards	7
7.00	Design requirements – makeup water treatment system	8
8.00	Design requirements – condensate polishing system	34
9.00	Design requirements – waste neutralization system	50
10.00	Testing and inspection	54
11.00	Painting and protection	54
12.00	Guarantees	55
13.00	Spare parts	57
14.00	Tools	57
15.00	Drawings	57
16.00	Evaluation factors	58
17.00	Delivery	58
18.00	Price	58
19.00	Technical data sheets	59
20.00	Exceptions to the specification	60

stance, has three sections on design requirements. Most specifications need only one. The project manager should issue a standard table of contents and permit controlled deviations from it. The project manager should also determine the section numbering scheme and section titles. Each paragraph should have a number to permit clear and unambiguous referencing. Items such as detailed format and typeface should also be determined by the project manager. Such matters do not usually affect the engineers, since they are clerical in nature.

Different industries have different format standards. The building industry is familiar with Construction Specification Institute format. The defense industry will be familiar with federal government, such as MIL specification, format. Clearer communication will result if industry format practices are followed.

Developing the Bidders List

The bidders list is a list of those vendors whose proposals will be solicited for each specification. It is usually prepared by the purchasing department because commercial matters are important in its development. It is important to procure equipment from vendors who have the financial resources to complete their contracts and have a reputation for reliable performance. They should also be financially stable enough that they can be expected to perform on their guarantees and warranties.

Although the bidders list is the responsibility of the purchasing department, the purchasing department cannot act without the continuous participation of the engineering department. Only the engineers understand whether the vendors suggested for inclusion on the bidders list actually produce the equipment the engineers need to procure. Therefore, although the purchasing department leads, the two departments actually produce the list in partnership.

It is usually necessary to prepare a bidders list for each project. In any continuing business, most of the bidders continue from project to project. However, new items keep appearing on the equipment list, necessitating new bidders. Also, bad experience with a bidder may force the bidder to be dropped and a substitute to be added. Some items, e.g., tanks, are often fabricated locally. Each new project location therefore influences the bidders list.

The project manager must ensure that the bidders list is developed for the project.

The bidders list should contain a sufficient number of vendors—at least three—for each specification to assure that a price close to the minimum possible is obtained. All bidders should be fully qualified both technically and commercially, since it is a waste of time to evaluate a proposal that is not going to be accepted. Adding bidders above those needed to get a good price is also a waste, since it adds to the cost of evaluating proposals.

The bidders list for an individual project is derived from the specification list. There must be bidders for each specification. One source of information for the project bidders list is the organization's generic bidders list, based on experience gained from previous projects. Every organization should have a bidders list to avoid repetitive bad experience with unreliable suppliers.

New bidders for the bidders list can initially be located by using directories such as *Sweet's Catalog* or *Thomas Register* and by perusing advertisements in the trade press. Also, if an organization has an active project, salespeople will find it and offer their products. One will also know of possible vendors from previous projects. One's colleagues are also a useful source of information. Once prospects are located, they must be investigated by both the engineers and the purchasing department. Much of the work can be done by telephone and discussions with salespeople. If the item is important enough, a visit to the factory will often yield useful information.

Some organizations, especially public bodies, do not use a bidders list. They will advertise in a public medium such as a newspaper and accept bids from anyone who wishes to compete. This process imposes two burdens on the specifying engineer. First, more complete specifications must be prepared, since no assumption can be made about the quality of the bidders. Second, all the bids must be evaluated. Since it is not unusual to have 20 or more bidders respond to one public solicitation, the evaluations can be a considerable burden. The burden can be reduced by screening the proposals and producing a short list of proposals considered to have a chance of being successful. A detailed evaluation is then made of only the proposals on the short list. One must be careful in screening proposals for a public bid, since the bidders may have a legal right to complain about mistreatment. It is necessary to leave a justifiable record of the evaluation effort.

A few public bodies will use bidders lists, rather than advertise for bids. In such cases, they are likely to have an elaborate procedure for evaluating prospective bidders, to avoid any unfairness and to justify their choices.

The bidders list should be prepared at the beginning of a project. It is often approved by the owner, whose experience in operating and maintaining plants often results in opinions about allowing vendors on the bidders list. The owner can often increase the efficiency of the operation by restricting vendors. This procedure makes management of spare parts inventory easier and increases the chance that maintenance and operating personnel will understand the needs of the equipment.

An alternative to a bidders list is prequalification of vendors. In this procedure, a request for qualifications is issued, describing the project in general terms and requesting that respondents describe their qualifications for performing it. The responses are evaluated, and the specification is then sent only to a limited number of firms deemed most qualified.

Preparing a Specification Effort Control Plan

Planning a specification effort is not complete until a means for ensuring that the effort will be completed as planned is in place. The schedule and the budget must be fulfilled. There are many systems for tracking the specification effort. On all but the smallest and simplest projects, computers are used to accumulate and organize data.

In actual practice, the specification control effort is integrated with the project control effort. The specification control effort is treated in isolation here to limit the scope of this book.

Computer systems are especially useful to track person-days. Most engineers are required to fill out time cards identifying the amount of time spent on each project, usually weekly. Sometimes such records afford a basis for billing a client. In organizations where a client is not billed for engineering time, the time card serves as a basis for cost accounting to the various projects being worked on. If time cards exist, they are also used for pay purposes.

The time card can also be used to track person-days spent on every individual specification. This is done by recording on the time card a number identifying a work item within the project. The biggest problem with this type of accounting is ensuring that the engineers properly record their work item numbers. If conscientiously recorded and processed, this information also provides a record of performance which can be used in future person-day estimates as well as in verifying that the current project is below budget.

Specification status is tracked by clerks who record milestones in the specification effort, such as the completion date of individual specifications. The clerks enter this data into the computer tracking system.

For both types of data, the computer system produces reports which project management can use to verify that the project is on schedule and under budget. If it is not, the record assists in analysis of the problem and taking corrective action. In a well-managed organization, the reports become available within a few days of the close of the time card recording period, permitting timely corrective action.

A well-managed organization will have a standard procedure for processing time cards and distributing the pertinent data on them to responsible personnel. Planning for the person-day control system then consists of adapting the standard system to the individual project. This function is performed by the project manager and his or her staff. Usually, they will assign work item numbers to the specifications and communicate them to the specification engineers and to the administrative group that operates the time card system. If every one does as he or she should, the system will then provide the required data.

Specification schedule status is usually controlled by a separate system. The project manager must also develop this system for the project. The staff should include clerks who compare the specification schedule with actual specification status and inform the project manager and the specification engineers of any discrepancies. Corrective action is then taken by them.

Imaginary Project 1 is simple enough that it can be controlled by checking specification completion against the schedule presented in Table 1-8. Time cards could be used in this case to verify that the people

Table 1-12. Imaginary Project 1: Specification Schedule Control Form

		Completion date[*]	
Specification		Scheduled	Actual
M1	Cooling tower	30	
M2	Centrifugal pumps	40	
M3	Chemical treatment system	34	
E1	Motor control center	30	
E2	Control panel	33	
S1	Electrical enclosure	40	
CM1	Electrical enclosure vent fan	55	
CM2	Electrical enclosure unit heater	55	
CM3	Piping and supports	57	
CM4	Valves	58	
CM5	Mechanical equipment erection	53	
CM6	Mechanical start-up and test	60	
CE1	Cables and conduit	55	
CE2	Instrumentation and control components	57	
CE3	Electrical installation	59	
CE4	Electrical start-up and test	60	
CS1	Concrete	57	
CS2	Structural steel	58	
CS3	Excavation and backfilling	59	
CS4	Electrical enclosure and erection	60	

[*]Working days after project initiation.

expected to be assigned to the job actually worked on it, but the time scale is so short that a direct inquiry will suffice. Unless the project manager is very good at keeping matters straight in his or her head, a specification tracking form as shown in Table 1-12 should be used to show progress.

2
Gathering Information

General

A specification can be viewed as a compendium of information. It follows that a primary step in writing a specification is gathering the information to be compiled in it. It comes from several diverse sources. Design information comes from the design team. Catalogs and salespeople supply information on available products. Local authorities may supply code requirements. Other information comes from the store of pertinent items the writer or the organization has gathered over the years.

An efficient specification writing effort depends on information for each specification being available when the writing of that specification begins. If the information is not readily available then, person-days will be wasted either seeking or waiting for it. This stipulation imposes two burdens on management..

First, project management must regulate the flow of information for the project. This may mean ensuring that the specification effort does not start until project information is available. Starting a specification effort using preliminary information often results in repeated effort, wasting person-days. It may also mean expediting project information so that it is available when the specification effort must be started to meet procurement schedules.

Second, engineering management must ensure that information applicable to a series of projects is available when needed. This category includes information on product availability, codes, standards, previous specifications, and so on. Such information tends to be accumulated over a period of time. Organizations new to specification writing tend to be comparatively innefficient because such information is lacking when needed. As an organization develops, such information becomes more readily available, leading to an increase in efficiency.

Information gathering will be discussed below in two time frames—the immediate one affecting the specification when it is being written and the long-term time frame.

Gathering Short-Term Information—General

Scheduling a specification effort is a project management effort. Project management will at least decide when each specification must be completed. Engineering management might decide when a specification must be started to meet that goal. Whoever decides when to start writing a specification should ask him or herself the questions listed in Table 2-1 before making a decision. The questions should be asked for each individual specification. Using Table 2-1 does not imply that all the information necessary for writing a specification must be available before writing begins. More information will be obtained as the effort continues. Table 2-1 represents a minimum, without which it is not even cost-efficient to begin.

In answering these questions, one implies a "first-time right" philosophy. The key to efficiency in any engineering effort is to commit a given action only once and do it right that time. It has been argued that engineering is performed by a series of approximations, repeating an operation several times, getting closer to the right answer each time. To an extent that procedure is necessary if the engineer is learning as he or she goes. Most commercial work is repetitive, and the first approximation should be the right one. This is particularly true for specification writing.

A specification is initiated by assigning an individual to write it. From

Table 2-1. Specification Initiation Checklist

1. Are design parameters final?
2. Is the product commercially available?
3. What kind of specification (commodity, catalog, or full) is required?
4. Are project instructions for format available?
5. Is the scope of the specification thoroughly understood?
6. Have all the items (e.g., all the transformers for a transformer specification) been identified?

that moment on, the specification writer is responsible and will be blamed if anything goes wrong.

If an engineer is methodical and knowledgeable, he or she will first gather as much as practical of the information needed before starting to write a specification. Less methodical engineers will start to write before they have the requisite information. They will be less efficient, first, because at times they will have to divert their attention from writing at times to get information they forgot about. Also, they may have to repeat work because newly acquired information does not fit with the work already done.

The first information a wise specification writer will investigate is the schedule. Being late in producing a specification results in much unwelcome attention. Management hates adverse surprises. It is much better to evaluate the schedule at the time the assignment is made and announce the possibility of lateness then, if a problem truly exists. At that time, it may be possible to adjust the project schedule to suit. However, unnecessary or too frequent announcements that a schedule is not feasible will result in a reputation for laziness and truculence. It is therefore necessary that the writer exercise care in the evaluation of the schedule.

The next piece of information the engineer should obtain is the commercial section. Two examples of procurement document organization were given in Chap. 1. In each of them, the commercial section can be defined as everything in the procurement except the technical requirements. To ensure clarity in the definition of a commercial section, the subjects usually covered are presented in Table 2-2. Table 2-2 must be accepted as typical, since the subjects actually covered are dependent on the industry the procuring organization is part of. Also, the organization of the commercial section can vary. Often, Instructions to Bidders contains information more logically placed in Special Conditions. The writers of commercial sections find it easier to vary the former section than the latter. It is often impossible to get the commercial and legal people to modify the commercial section to suit the needs of the technical people, so the specification must usually be written to accommodate it. It is necessary that the specification writer be familiar with the commercial section so that the commercial section and the specification do not contradict one another. Also, the engineer should prepare the specification as part of the procurement document, ensuring as much as possible that all necessary subjects are covered somewhere in the document. This practice is necessary to avoid trouble later in the procurement cycle.

Gathering information on the scope of the specification is an obvious

Table 2-2. Commercial Section Contents

Instructions to bidders

  Abbreviated scope of the work

  Definitions

  Date and address of proposal submittal

  Information to be submitted with proposal

  Method of submittal (e.g., sealed envelope)

  Bid validity period

  Method of evaluation

Proposal This section can take many forms. Some examples are

  (A) A short form the bidder fills in with the price

  (B) A set of forms the bidder fills in with answers to commercial and technical questions

  This section may be omitted if the bidder is permitted to submit the proposal in his or her own format.

Contract agreement This section states the kernel of the contract. It may refer to other sections for completion. It is designed to be signed by the successful bidder and the owner.

General conditions This section contains commercial and legal conditions set in all procurement contracts used by the owner. Subjects discussed may include

  Ownership of drawings and specifications

  Changes

  Claims

  Limits of liability

  Occupational safety and health

  Laws, regulations, etc.

  Patents and royalties

  Delays and extension of time

  Insurance

  Drawings by contractor

  Technical direction

  Termination for convenience of the owner

  Passage of title

  Meetings

Special conditions This section will cover commercial and legal matters which apply only to this procurement action. Items which may be included are

---

Table 2-2. Commercial Section Contents (*Continued*)

Work by others

Site

Drawings and data by vendor

Reports by vendor

Schedule

Inspection and shop tests

Status of proprietary information

Warranties

Delays

necessity. The scope must be understood in several terms. The equipment item number and name for each component to be included in the specification must be determined. There is the question of "battery limits," that is, the point where the scope of the specification under consideration ends and the scope of the next one begins. In a pump specification, for example, is the motor to be included? Is the base plate to be included? Are the anchor bolts to be included? The answers to these questions can vary from project to project. There is also the question of when the vendor relinquishes responsibility. Does the vendor simply furnish the equipment, with the owner taking on the chore of shipping? Perhaps the vendor furnishes and delivers. Then again, in limited cases, the vendor furnishes, delivers, installs, and tests the equipment. These questions are often settled at least partially on the basis of project policy.

The specification engineer must also obtain the standard format requirements from the project manager. It saves time if the standard format is used from the beginning, rather than being converted when the specification is nearly done.

Codes, Standards, and Regulations

A standard is a difficult term to define as it applies to specifications. Most dictionaries only hint at this usage of the word. Apparently, the difficulty is that this use of the word is both very general and vague. To try to summarize the engineering use of the word, a *standard* is an extended definition. A *dimensional standard* can be defined as a document that describes agreed-upon dimensions for a material. As an example, American National Standards Institute (ANSI) standard B36.10 defines standard dimensions for stainless-steel pipe. The concept of a standard extends to other parameters besides dimensions. One standard that is often used is the one that defines camera film speeds. Other parameters described by standards are chemical composition of alloys and voltage levels for electrical equipment. Standards do not usually contain recommendations for use. ANSI standard B36.10, for example, defines the dimensions and chemistry of stainless-steel pipe, but does not recommend when to use stainless steel instead of carbon steel.

A *code*, in engineering terms, is a prescription of how things should be done. Two pervasive codes are the National Electrical Code and the American Society of Mechanical Engineers (ASME) Boiler and Pressure Vessel Code. Both govern design and construction in their respective fields. Both direct engineers in how to design and build equipment and systems in their respective areas of responsibility.

Although a difference can be distinguished between codes and standards in theory, this difference is not well observed in practice. Many codes, for example the ASME Power Piping Code, are published as standards. Therefore, many engineers lump these two kinds of documents together and treat them as one category. Some standards are in the form of specifications. For example, the American Society for Testing and Materials issues standards of this type. It is useful to treat them as standards because they define what is meant by, for example, type A536 alloy steel plate.

The engineer must not only know what codes and standards will apply to the specification but must also be aware of how they are to be applied. The engineer should know, for example, that although American standards and codes are relatively rigid, foreign ones often include provision for supplementary agreement between the vendor and the customer.

It is unreasonable to expect specification writers to understand thoroughly all the codes and standards they specify. There are too many codes and standards, and they are too involved. It is sufficient if the writer understands how and why they apply to the specification.

Many organizations in the United States publish codes and standards. A partial list is given in Table 2-3. Since the United States is a free society, anyone or any organization can write a document and label it a standard. Conversely, anyone is free to call out or omit any standard in a specification. In general, standards are applied because engineers find them useful or because they are required by a governmental law or regulation. Another possibility is that an insurance company or a financial institution insists that a code or standard be applied.

Table 2-3. American Organizations Publishing Standards and Codes

Air Conditioning and Refrigeration Institute

American Bureau of Shipping

American Concrete Institute

American Institute of Architects

American Institute of Chemical Engineers

American Institute of Mining, Metallurgical and Petroleum Engineers

American Institute of Steel Construction

American National Standards Institute

American Nuclear Society

American Petroleum Institute

American Society of Heating, Refrigeration and Air Conditioning Engineers

American Society of Mechanical Engineers

American Society for Quality Control

American Society for Testing and Materials

American Water Works Association

American Welding Society

American Wind Energy Association

Illuminating Engineers Society

Institute of Electrical and Electronic Engineers

Instrument Society of America

Insulated Power Cable Engineers Society

Manufacturers Standardization Society

National Bureau of Standards

National Electrical Manufacturers Association

National Fire Protection Association

Pipe Fabrication Institute

Society of Automotive Engineers

Society for Non-Destructive Testing

Tubular Exchanger Manufacturers Association

Underwriters' Laboratories, Inc.

The ANSI was formed to bring order to the world of standards. It provides a standard methodology for developing standards, which ensures that representatives of all parties likely to be affected by a standard are included in its development. It also coordinates the development of standards, sees that they are published in a standard format, and provides a catalog of existing standards. Other nations have similar organizations. The International Standards Organization coordinates all the national standards organizations.

By *regulations* we mean documents issued by a government body which derive their authority from law. They are issued by all levels of government. Local governments will often have building regulations, unfortunately sometimes labeled building codes. The federal government has a very extensive system of regulations. A partial list of federal government bodies issuing regulations important to specifications is given in Table 2-4. Federal regulations will often reference codes and standards. Federal regulations are collected in a series of books called the *Code of Federal Regulations.*

Closely linked to regulations are the laws themselves, which can also reference codes and standards. The ASME Boiler and Pressure Vessel Code, for example, is required by law in most of the United States.

Writers must be especially careful to ensure that they have information on the local regulations, such as zoning laws, environmental laws, sanitation codes, and local construction codes. These regulations can vary considerably from locality to even adjacent locality. Some local areas can be so restrictive as to require proof that the external appearance of a building is aesthetically consistent with neighboring buildings.

States also have laws and regulations which affect specifications. Many of them mandate the ASME Boiler and Pressure Vessel Code.

Table 2-4. Federal Government Agencies Issuing
Regulations Important to Specifications

Agency	CFR title
Consumer Product Safety Commission	16
Environmental Protection Agency	31
Federal Communications Commission	4
Federal Highway Commission	7
Food and Drug Administration	21
Mine Safety and Health Administration	30
Occupational Safety and Health Administration	29
Rural Electrification Administration	7
United States Coast Guard	33
United States Nuclear Regulatory Commission	10

They also often have industrial hygiene and occupational safety standards.

Part of the information-gathering process is determining what standards, codes, regulations, and laws apply to the specification at hand. They may apply because they are legally mandated. Then too, codes and standards can be referenced because they describe a standard of quality, because it is more convenient to reference a standard than to duplicate its requirements in the specification, or because citing the code or standard will make the specified equipment consistent with adjoining equipment.

Design Information

The design of any project starts with site conditions, which are important to specifications in many ways. For equipment located out of doors, the site climate is important. The site climate is also important for heating, ventilating, and air-conditioning equipment even when it is located indoors. For equipment or buildings with their own foundations, site soil conditions are important. Site information must be available at the start of a project and, if applicable to the item being specified, should be sought out.

Information developed in the course of project design is often used as input to specifications. For example, the design parameters of equipment to be specified must be obtained from the design. Until the final parameters are determined, there is little point in starting the specification and especially little point in asking for proposals. When starting to write a specification, therefore, the engineer will seek out the required design information from the design engineers and ascertain that it is final.

Features

The requirements for a piece of equipment can be divided into two broad categories: parameters and features. *Parameters* are numbers with units that define the performance and other requirements of the equipment. Examples for a transformer might be the kilovolt-ampere output and a limitation on height or other dimensions. *Features* are described in words that specify what kind of equipment is required. An example for a heat exchanger might be a requirement for seamless, rather than welded, tubes, or a clad, rather than bare, tube sheet. Parameters are usually defined anew for each project. Features may remain the same for corresponding equipment on successive projects.

Definition of features is the activity for which specification engineers really earn their salaries. Features govern the value, cost, and availability of the equipment. Definition of features requires good judgment and knowledge. The equipment must be adequate for the application but not overly complex. Specifying features too strictly increases cost. Specifying them too loosely results in low-quality equipment.

Good specification engineers will already possess most of the feature information needed to write a specification, at least in their area of specialty, when they are assigned to write specifications. Good specification engineers invest much of their spare time reviewing literature and asking people for information which will help them write future specifications. Much of the information needed is gained through operating and maintenance experience. Since such information is often received orally from the operators and maintenance personnel, it is often fragmentary and anecdotal. To be useful, it must be understood as well as is practical.

It is not sufficient to rely completely on past information, since technology and circumstances are continuously changing. Knowledge must be constantly renewed.

Assuming the engineer assigned to a specification does not know everything about the features to be specified, he or she must seek the information elsewhere. The best source of information is an engineer experienced in the equipment being specified, possibly the specification engineer's supervisor. Such engineers have much information in their heads and often know where to find information they do not have.

A second source of information is existing specifications, perhaps standard specifications, previous specifications prepared by the same organization, or specifications from other organizations. Again, such information must be used with care. What was appropriate for some other project may not be appropriate for this one. Blind copying is not a good idea. The engineer should ideally understand everything put into a specification.

Another indispensable source of information is vendor catalogs. They will certainly describe what features are available and standard. Some catalogs contain a great deal of technical information as well. If the reputation of the vendor is known, some judgments can be made regarding the value of the features described.

Some vendors have written books on their products. These books differ from catalogs in that they are more general, more technical, and do not itemize the products. A list of some useful vendor books is given in Table 2-5. They are often a valuable and unique source of information.

Table 2-5. Vendor Books

Combustion Fossil Power Systems (1981)
Joseph G. Singer, editor
Combustion Engineering, Inc.
1000 Prospect Hill Road
Windsor, Connecticut

Fan Engineering, Eighth Edition (1983)
Robert Jorgenson, editor
Buffalo Ferge Company
Buffalo, New York

Steam (1972)
Babcock & Wilcox Company
161 East 42nd Street
New York, New York

Steel Design Manual (1986)
by R. T. Brockenbrough and B. G. Johnson
United States Steel Corporation
Pittsburgh, Pennsylvania

Swagelock Tube Fitting and Installation Manual (1985)
by F. J. Callahan
Crawford Fitting Company
29500 Solon Road
Solon, Ohio

Whiting Crane Handbook, Fourth Edition (1979)
by William M. Weaver
Whiting Corporation
Harvey, Illinois

One should also seek out salespeople to get feature information. They are all biased in favor of their own products, but then many of them know their own products very well. Many salespeople are also fine technical people. Any specification writer can learn a great deal from salespeople. Salespeople also have the advantage that, unlike books and catalogs, they answer questions. Most salespeople prefer to dwell on the advantages of their products, but by adroit questioning, one can determine the disadvantages as well and define situations where the products should not be used. Most salespeople also consider it unethical to criticize their competitors directly, but they will often discuss their competitors' faults if questioned directly and carefully.

Finally, not to be ignored is the information contained in published literature—books, periodicals, government reports, and so forth. There is a wealth of information there on equipment features.

Long-Term Information Gathering—General

It is patently inefficient to start an information search every time a specification is to be written. As much as practical, a writer should have a readily available source of information, in other words, a library. The library should contain information deemed likely to be used in future specifications.

A library collection is a dynamic affair. New information, especially new editions of codes and standards, is continuously added. To an extent, old information needs to be continuously deleted, since it takes up space and makes it more difficult to find the really useful information. Old catalogs should be culled rapidly, since many of the products in them are no longer available. Old codes should never be deleted. They may not be needed for specifications, but they may be needed to design modifications for existing equipment.

A library must be well organized. Data that cannot be found may as well not exist. Time spent looking for information is time wasted.

A library needs a librarian, someone to maintain order and to order and receive new materials. The librarian can be full- or part-time, depending on the size of the collection. Few specification support libraries are large or complex enough to justify a professionally trained librarian.

The librarian should report to an engineering manager. No librarian can be expected to have a complete understanding of the engineering significance attached to the library's contents. The engineering manager must take the library duties seriously enough to give the librarian adequate guidance.

The library handles several media. Catalogs, codes, and standards generally come as hard copy. Sometimes they are available as microfiche, a form more compact to store but more awkward to use. Some standards and standard specifications are now becoming available as read-only compact discs, an even more compact form. The future will probably bring more electronic storage.

In most cases, the library will be a general one, serving the entire organization, not just the specification writers.

The organization's past and standard specifications should be available to the specification writers. They might be in the library or might also be available in the offices of selected senior engineering personnel, on the theory that they will be more available to the writers. If the organization is big enough, there may be a dedicated specification word processing group. This group should have copies of the specifications they have processed. At present, such copies are likely to be on electronic media. If the writer obtains such documents in electronic form, it should be a copy, not the original, to avoid contaminating the record with modifications.

Most specification writers will have their own information collections. A person with a proper professional attitude will insist on it. It is appropriate that he or she should do so. However, company information should be in the library where it is accessible to everyone. The organization should not require specification writers to provide all their own information. Some of the information is very expensive. It is wasteful to have several copies of one document in an organization when one copy in the library can be shared.

Catalogs and Brochures

Manufacturers' catalogs are vital to the specification writer. They record what products are available and who makes them. They also usually contain prices, although the published prices may need a correction factor available separately from the manufacturer. Catalogs are usually obtained at no cost from the manufacturer. They should be maintained in the library, even if the manufacturer gives them to an individual specification writer. Generally, when receiving catalogs, the writer is acting as a representative of the organization.

If a manufacturer makes standard products, the products will likely be in the catalog. If a manufacturer produces services or custom equipment, descriptions of the range of services or goods produced may be in a catalog. Alternatively, the document which provides this information might be termed a brochure.

Specifications

The best help a specification writer can get is a copy of a specification on the same, or nearly the same, subject. It is ideal if the sample specification is in the same format as the required one. Specification writers will therefore collect specifications they think might prove useful. Good specification writers will try to keep a copy of every specification they write or have a part in writing.

There are other ways of getting prototype specifications. Sometimes a writer receives one because his or her organization is bidding on a project. Sometimes a client will provide one as an example of how to meet his or her needs. If obtained legitimately, one should try to keep copies of specifications which might prove useful.

If an organization writes custom specifications in the client's format, copies of all specifications written should be in the library for guidance in writing future specifications. If they are in the word processing system, they should be retrievable in electronic form to minimize rewriting and retyping.

Standard Specifications

A well-planned organization will have a set of standard specifications on subjects likely to recur in its business. Ideally, writing a new specification consists of adding new data sheets to the existing specification. It may be that modifications to the text need to be made to suit the project or the client's format. In any event, the standard specifications need to be available to the specification writers.

The most obvious way of storing standard specifications is as hard copy. If the specification writers are versatile enough, it is better to let them use copies of specifications on floppy disks. They can then modify the standard specifications as necessary at their own terminals. The originals should remain under the library's control so that they cannot be modified inadvertently.

Standard specifications from external organizations should also be in the library, if applicable to the organization's business. Two examples are SPECTEXT from the Construction Specifications Institute and Masterspec from the American Institute of Architects.

Laws and Regulations

Laws, per se, are not often cited in specifications. Accordingly, they need not be collected in the library. Regulations, which are rules published by governmental agencies under the authority of a law, are often so cited. A specification library should contain at least those government regulations which affect its business. Federal regulations are published in a document called "Code of Federal Regulations," available from the U.S. Government Printing Office. It is printed in several volumes, each of which is republished once a year. In the interim, new regulations are published daily in the *Federal Register*. In some industries, the regulatory climate is so dynamic that it is necessary to subscribe to the *Federal Register*.

The "Code of Federal Regulations" is divided into sections called titles. Table 2-4 shows the titles for several government agencies important to specifications.

State and local regulations are sometimes also important to specifications. Accordingly, they should also be added to the library selectively.

3
Production Management

General

Specification production means not just writing the specification but all the steps required to carry out the plan as described in Chap. 1 up to the point of issuing the specification for bid. This is a cooperative effort, with many people involved to perform the work and to ensure that the specifications are produced on schedule and within budget, are of the appropriate quality, and fit the needs of the project.

The key to meeting the goals of a specification effort is careful, balanced management. Balanced management means a careful and realistic plan, good communication, control through knowledge of what is actually occurring on the project, and judicious deployment of available resources. It should be based on the first-time right concept. Work repeated is time wasted. Work should not be started until all the conditions for its successful completion are in place. Information from prior project activities should be available before the specification work is released. Thus, it may be necessary to pursue the required information aggressively at the right time to ensure that the project schedule is met. To use another buzz word, management must be "proactive," that is, the managers must use foresight and detect and set right problems before they cause an irrevocable loss of productivity and schedule time.

A flowchart for specification production is shown in Fig. 3-1. This chart is designed to show the people involved in specification production and the relationships among them. It is a generalized chart, typical of the procedures in an engineering organization. A very small organi-

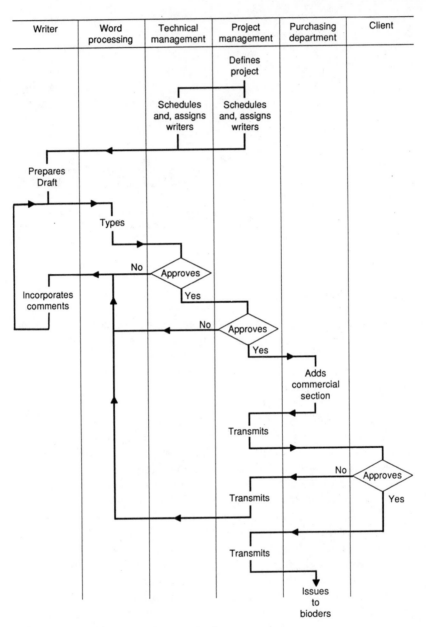

42

Processes

Figure 3-1. Specification production procedure

zation would not have such an elaborate procedure since, in that case, one person might fulfill more than one of the roles shown.

Most organizations with a multiproject work load use a matrix organization. A project management organization exists to execute individual projects. A permanent technical organization also exists to provide continuity, a supply of engineers and architects to assign to contracts as they arise, a repository for standards, and specialized technical knowledge and quality control. The engineer or architect on a project has responsibilities toward both project and technical managements. The power of each management organization varies depending on the firm's practices and situation. If the firm has a few large and long-duration projects, project management tends to dominate. If the projects are many and short term, technical management tends to dominate. Both management organizations must cooperate to perform a project.

In some cases, the matrix nature of the organization may not be apparent. If the projects are very small and short, the project managers may be engineers or architects working on a temporary assignment and reporting to engineering or architectural management. Even in this case, a project manager exists and the project management functions are carried out. Virtually the only case where the process depicted in Fig. 3-1 does not apply is the one where one person performs all the functions.

Titles will vary. The ones used in Fig. 3-1 are appropriate for an engineering organization. In an architectural organization, many of the functions are performed by architects, rather than engineers. The project manager may be called project architect or project engineer.

As with any procedure, the one shown in Fig. 3-1 will be facilitated by informal talk among the participants. For example, the specification writer and his or her managers should discuss the type of specification to be produced, its format, experience to be applied, and principles to be used, so that approval will be facilitated. Lack of understanding between the writer and managers may result in the specification being modified and retyped several times before approval is obtained.

Figure 3-1 identifies six major groups participating in specification production. The role of each is discussed in this chapter.

Project Management

In an ideal, well-managed effort, production begins when planning is complete. In the environment of the present-day engineering business, the preliminary design, equipment list, specification list, person-day estimate, and overall schedule should be developed in the proposal stage.

The project may then go into a dormant period while the customer considers the proposal. A period of negotiations may then follow. Since proposal costs need to be minimized, preparation of detailed schedules, including the specification schedule, and the bidders list would likely be deferred until a contract has been obtained. Usually, since some features of the project will change during contract negotiations, it is necessary to review and update all the organizing documents prepared during the proposal phase after the engineering contract is granted. In any event, soon after the contract stage begins, the following items should be in an up-to-date and valid condition: equipment list, specification list, person-day estimate, specification schedule, and control procedure. Activities relative to the specification effort during this phase of the project are shown schematically in Table 3-1. Architectural projects go through a similar start-up phase. The major difference between an engineering project and an architectural project is that equipment is less prominent in an architectural project. A discrete equipment list usually does not exist.

In an ideal world, administering the specification effort from the completion of planning on would be a simple matter of carrying out the plan. In practice, the plan must be modified continuously as design details are defined and as other new facts are determined. One measure of

Table 3-1. Early Stages in Project Development
(Specification Aspects Only)

Customer	Contractor
Prepares and issues request for proposals	
	Prepares and submits proposal
	Information prepared includes
	Cost estimate
	Overall schedule
	Preliminary design
	Equipment list
	Specification list
	Person-day estimate
Evaluates proposals	
Selects contractor	
Negotiates contract	Negotiates contract
	Executes contract, including
	Specification schedule
	Detail design
	Final equipment list
	Worker schedule
	Project control system

management quality is the number of modifications that must be made in the plan. The smaller the number of changes, the higher the quality. Plan modifications are a form of work being done over, and are therefore time wasted. Also, plan modifications are symptomatic of technical work being done over and are therefore technical time being wasted. If the plan were done right the first time, none of this waste would occur.

When a contract has been obtained, there is a natural tendency to start work immediately in a disorganized manner, since the project schedule has started running. This tendency must be resisted. Instead, project management must ensure that the effort is well organized before any work is started. Time spent in organization will save time in the project schedule and effort as well.

In many projects, selected vital specifications may be completed before planning is complete. In a power plant, for example, the steam generator and the turbine may be specified in the proposal stage. These two items have long lead times, so the project schedule may have to be developed around them. Also, many plant design details are determined by these components. Finally, these components are important in the capital cost of the plant. It may be desirable to have a firm price for them before making the project proposal. Production of most specifications will be deferred to the contract stage, if practical, to reduce proposal cost. Proposal costs are a dead loss if the contract is not obtained.

The primary mission of management is the judicious application of resources. In an engineering organization, this means fundamentally that engineers in the right numbers and with the right talents are assigned to the project at the right time. In determining these assignments, the management is guided by the schedule and the person-day estimate. The performance of the effort is judged by the output of the control system. If engineers are assigned in accordance with the schedule and the required production is not obtained, corrective action must be taken. It can be overtime, more engineers, different engineers, different managers, or modification of the plan.

Assigning engineers is not a mere numbers game. Engineers vary in both their knowledge and capability. To obtain proper results, the engineer must be matched to the work required. The ability to perform such matches is tempered by the availability of engineers. The best ones for the mission at hand may be assigned elsewhere and may therefore be unavailable. Also, it makes sense to use the same engineers for successive assignments on the same project. This practice is good psychologically, since it builds teamwork and since engineers like to see their work through to completion. Also, engineers will develop a knowledge of the project. If new engineers are assigned, they must spend time becoming familiar with the project. It is therefore good practice to keep the same engineers on the project continuously, even if they are not the optimum ones from the point of view of knowledge and competence.

The project mangagement department takes the lead in most of the activities outlined above. It will draw on the technical organization for the information needed. The technical organization will have a particular interest in person-day estimates, schedule, and assignment of engineers, since they will be held responsible for performance of these aspects of the project.

Assignment of engineers can be a sensitive subject and must be a joint responsibility between project management and technical management. Assignment of an engineer or architect to an individual specification is usually a function of technical management.

A major activity of project management during specification production is maintaining control over status and schedule. Figure 3-1 shows that each specification undergoes a multistep production process. On a large project, which may have 200 or more specifications, a great deal of effort must be devoted to ascertaining continuously the status of each specification, comparing actual status to scheduled status, and taking whatever corrective action is necessary.

Manual methods for specification control will suffice for a small project. A form suitable for Imaginary Project 1 was shown in Table 1-12. This form will suffice for such a small project, where the project manager can keep track of progress largely in his or her head. For a larger project, or one with an unalert project manager, such a form may lead to reactive management. The manager may not realize that the project is in trouble until he or she encounters dates for actual specification completion that are later than the scheduled dates. For a somewhat larger project, a form like that shown in Table 3-2 would be better. It provides for identifying the writer. The first clue the manager may have of schedule problems is that he or she cannot identify the writer. A record of start date is also valuable. If the specification is not started, it cannot be finished. Actually, record of a start is subject to abuse. The writer can claim to have started, then go off and do something else. In a large project, intermediate goals should also be recorded.

A specification project manager should be a leader and a coordinator and should be able to secure completion of the work economically and on time. This function requires a large amount of tact in getting the various parts of the organization to work together, as well as leadership in accomplishing project objectives. The manager should be able to judge the work in terms of project goals and be able to judge the quality of the work in general, although ultimate responsibility for quality rests with technical management. It is implicit that the project manager is a

Table 3-2. Imaginary Project 1: Specification Control Form

		Dates			
Spec. no.	Writer	Scheduled	Started	First draft	Final draft
M1	Smith	1/30			
M2	Smith	2/9			
M3	Patel	2/3			
E1	Brown	1/30			
E2	Brown	2/2			
S1	Jones	2/9			
CM1	Smith	2/24			
CM2	Smith	2/24			
CM3	Smith	2/26			
CM4	Smith	2/27			
CM5	Smith	2/22			
CM6	Smith	3/1			
CE1	Brown	2/24			
CE2	Brown	2/26			
CE3	Brown	2/28			
CE4	Brown	3/1			
CS1	Jones	2/26			
CS2	Jones	2/27			
CS3	Jones	2/28			
CS4	Jones	3/1			

good communicator, with the emphasis on oral communications. The project manager is also a methodical organizer, maintaining control over all parts of the specification project.

The Writer

The assigned writer is the foundation of the specification effort. He or she is the prime mover. Productivity and quality originate from the writer's efforts. Quality can be built into a specification after it has been drafted, through review and comments by other engineers or architects and supervisors. This is an inefficient and demoralizing process. It is much better if the engineer has the ability and makes the effort to do an adequate job in the first instance. Productivity cannot be added after the fact, since the time is already gone. It can be enhanced during the writer's effort if he or she has all the information and tools needed to work with and has the motivation and morale to do a good job. This first-time right philosophy is the key to economical specification preparation.

The writer is responsible for preparing the specification. The original product is a draft of the document. This draft can take a number of forms. If the specification is entirely original, it can be a longhand document or, if the engineer is so inclined and adept, a printout from a word processor. For a less original specification, it might be a cut-and-paste job, with many words and paragraphs taken from previous specifications, interspersed with original words to suit the needs of the extant project. Again, if the engineer has the ability and inclination to use a word processor, the cut-and-paste work may have been done electronically, producing a smooth document. An even less original specification might be a marked-up previous specification. Finally, the least original and most efficient form is a standard specification with project-specific data sheets added. In any case, the writer produces the draft. Even if the writer prepared the specification on a word processor, word processing personnel will usually redo it to make the format conform to project standards.

The specification is based on information extracted from project design documents. Design documents are items that describe the design but are not specifications. Examples are drawings, system descriptions, and tabulations such as valve lists and instrument lists. If a specification effort is differentiated from the design effort, it is here that the transition occurs.

The writer must first verify that he or she has truly been furnished all the necessary information. If not, it is up to the writer to seek out the missing information. This includes verification that the equipment or service to be specified exists in the commercial market.

There is no point in writing a specification for something that cannot be procured economically. It is surprising how often engineers or architects will require features that no vendor will furnish as a standard item. Some catalog review or a few telephone calls to vendors will often prevent writing a uneconomic specification. If the designers want a specification written that cannot be fulfilled in the commercial market, it is the writer's responsibility to notify management of the situation promptly so that a decision on how to proceed can be reached without delaying the project.

A good practice is to hold the writer totally responsible for the content, schedule, and person-days spent on a specification. It does the project no good if a writer is allowed to complain that the specification is late because another individual did not perform. At this point, the project has already suffered a financial loss. Any complaints should be made before the project suffers. It may seem to be harsh to hold the writer totally responsible, but it is the only way to achieve a healthy project. Since the writer is to be held responsible, it is necessary that the writer be clearly informed of the budget and schedule for the work when he or she is assigned.

The writer is also responsible for coordination with other technical personnel on the same project. This includes coordination with the design engineers or architects to ensure that the specification carries out the designer's intent. It also includes coordination with other discipline specification writers working on the same project. A mechanical specification writer will generally, for example, need to coordinate with the electrical engineer to ensure that the motors driving mechanical equipment meet project requirements. One way such coordination is performed is by having inserts for specifications. The electrical department may, for example, furnish an insert on motor requirements to go into mechanical and chemical specifications. If seismic requirements exist, the structural department will prepare sections on that subject to be inserted in the electrical, mechanical, and their own structural specifications. Each writer is responsible for obtaining and using all such inserts and all other necessary information from other disciplines.

Sometimes, to ensure that each specification includes the requirements of other disciplines, an interdisciplinary review step is included in the production procedure. This device should be used sparingly and selectively. Most information in a specification is of concern only to the originating discipline. Time spent by a second discipline in reviewing it is often time wasted. The original specification writer should therefore request interdisciplinary reviews only when there is a need and should limit them only to the pertinent portion of the specification. The writer will be held responsible for the total specification.

On the other hand, if a writer recognizes the need for input from another discipline in a timely manner and asks for it, it is the responsibility of that discipline to provide it. The mechanical department cannot be expected to guess at electrical requirements, nor should the electrical department be expected to guess at circuit breaker sizes required to provide power to motors driving mechanical equipment. If the planning effort was properly executed, person-days are in the budget and time is in the schedule for such interdiscipline efforts.

The writer should also be aware of the commercial requirements the purchasing department will add to the specification. There are many commercial requirements that the specification writer does not have the time to learn about thoroughly. It is best to leave them to the judgment of the commercial personnel. However, there are often a few items that will concern the writer. Sometimes, for example, the commercial section will contain some of the requirements for drawing submittals such as the number of reproducibles and prints to be submitted. It will also contain instructions to bidders, which define information to be submitted in the proposal. Some of this information is used by the engineer or architect to evaluate proposals. Since it is very difficult to change the commercial section, the technical section will have to conform to it.

It can be seen from Fig. 3-1 that the draft is not the end of the writer's effort. The writer must also incorporate reviewers' comments. This should not be a mere mechanical exercise. The writer should incorporate only those comments which are improvements. To do otherwise would be to lower quality. On the other hand, a writer should not be allowed to disregard comments without good reason. If a writer cannot defend his or her product, he or she has likely made a wrong decision.

A seeming detail that can cause considerable controversy is the relationship between writers and the word processing department. A little tact will help this interface enormously. The copy delivered to word processing should be legible and well enough organized that the word processing operator can follow it. All too often it is not, leaving the word processing personnel to guess what the writer wanted to say. At the same time, it must be recognized that writers are more expensive than word processors, so the latter should accept all the burdens they reasonably can.

The ideal specification writer is, first of all, a good communicator, especially in writing. The product must be clear and understandable. Good oral communication is also necessary to fulfill the writer's coordination responsibility. The writer is expected to be knowledgeable about the equipment or service being specified and should know enough about the system the specified equipment will be contained in so that he or she can specify the right equipment. The writer is not, however, responsible for system operation unless an entire system is specified. The specification writer should be industrious and capable of independent work. He or she will be supervised, but since supervision is an additional cost, it will be the minimum necessary to achieve production and quality.

Technical Management

Project management and technical management work as a team to complete a specification effort. Project management sets the tasks. They define the scope of the work and set the person-day budget and schedules. They also control programs, that is, gather and organize data which shows whether project goals are likely to be met. Corrective action is taken by the appropriate section of management.

Fundamentally, in the short term, technical management ensures that the goals set by project management are met. With regard to a specification effort, this means that adequate specifications are prepared on time and within budget. The budget must be competitive.

Meeting a competitive budget requires foresight. The tools required to write specifications efficiently must be available when needed. For example, a library was discussed in Chap. 2. It is technical management's responsibility to see that the library contains the right information. In most organizations, an administrative department operates the library. However, an administrative department cannot be expected to know what should be in the library. All the administration can do, and it is important, is to keep the library orderly. It must be possible to find information in the library. If an item is out on loan, the librarian must be able to find the item and retrieve it.

Another example is maintaining standard specifications. Existing specifications must be kept updated in accordance with current technology, and new ones must be written to meet anticipated project needs. To promote efficiency, technical management must also ensure that specification writers use existing standard specifications to the maximum extent practical. An ideal specification effort would be one where all specifications were standard, with only data sheets changed.

The library and standard specifications are not usually sufficient. Frequently, specifications need to be written on subjects not covered in the standards. In this case, it may be that the subject was covered on some previous project. Technical management is expected to know about these precedents and make the previous specification available for use as a basis for the new specification.

A continuous turnover in engineers and architects exists. New ones graduate from college, old ones retire, others change positions, and organizations grow and shrink. Therefore, a continuous process of learning occurs. It is naive to suppose that perfectly knowledgeable specification writers exist. More commonly, although the specification engineer knows a great deal about the equipment or service to be specified, a source of information to fill in the gaps in his or her knowledge is needed. This is one of the functions of engineering management.

As part of the first-time right philosophy, it is technical management's responsibility to assess the assigned writer's ability, competence, and knowledge at the time writing a specification is initiated. They then must confirm that the writer has all the tools needed to perform the task. The writer is expected to take the initiative in securing information. Management confirms that the writer understands the task and knows about all the pertinent information. Only if both parties assume a proactive stance can it be expected that the specification will be written right the first time. Once expended, person-days cannot be recovered. Good productivity is obtained only if writing is initiated correctly.

Good quality is also better assured by a proactive stance on both management's and the writer's parts. The writer has prime responsibility for quality and is expected to provide self-criticism and self-checking. Only after the writer is satisfied with the product should it be released for review by others. During production, if the writer considers the work lacking in any respect, he or she should seek guidance from management or peers.

Technical management must supervise specification writers. They must anticipate or detect early any problems the writers might have in meeting the schedule, budget, or quality. Then they must take action to resolve the problems. Management should be proactive; that is, they should be active in detecting problems early, rather than waiting until they become obvious. This latter, reactive, course of action results in inefficiency.

Technical management also ensures that the writers assigned to a project are as competent as practical. For engineers or architects fresh out of college, this implies training in specification writing. For newly hired, experienced personnel, this means training in company procedures and resources. Training may be formal or on the job. In the latter case, individual job budgets will suffer. From a corporate point of view, on-the-job training still might be the right choice since it can be tailored to the case at hand and can be more efficient than formal training.

Efficiency in producing specifications demands maximum reuse of existing knowledge. Ideally, specifications would be reused from project to project, with only data sheets changed. This ideal cannot often be realized, due to changing conditions and technology. Technical management provides knowledge of what elements from past projects exist and are available for reuse. They maintain files of this information in a retrievable form.

Closely allied to providing information to specification writers is the function of quality control. Quality is primarily the writer's responsibility. Company practices, for efficiency's sake, should be based on this premise. However, even a perfectly knowledgeable writer will have lapses. He or she may omit items from the specification or make errors. A system of quality control is necessary. It is usually provided by technical management review of the specification. If the manager has been properly proactive during specification preparation and if the writer has been properly conscientious about writing the specification, the review should result in few changes to the specification.

Technical management also assures that specification engineers are available for assignment to projects. This function requires maintaining liaison with the project managers to determine each project's need for specification engineers. The liaison must be proactive. Technical management has to actively seek out project management's needs so that the right specification writers can be made available when needed.

Many projects require that specifications be stamped by a licensed professional engineer or architect. Such a requirement can arise from the law where the project is located if the specification affects public safety. There is also such a requirement in some parts of the ASME Boiler and Pressure Vessel Code. Sometimes clients want specifications stamped as an extra assurance of quality. Individual equipment specifications are usually stamped by a technical manager, since this is considered part of quality control and since the manager is considered to be in responsible charge of the work. For the most part, specification writers are not licensed personnel. Specifications which represent the totality of a project may be stamped by project management. The person who stamps a specification accepts legal responsibility for it as it affects public safety.

Engineering managers need to be highly qualified in technical matters since they are responsible for quality control and since they serve as technical advisors. They also have to make up for any lack in technical quality on the part of the specification engineers. They need to be good communicators. Written communication ability is necessary because they must ensure that the specifications are clear and effective. They must be good oral communicators to fulfill their supervisory duties and to coordinate with the project management group, especially in the planning phase.

Purchasing Department

The purchasing department is generally independent of both the project management and the engineering departments. It is staffed by commercial people who are generally not engineers. Its basic function is to procure equipment, materials, and services at the right price, quality, and time to meet project requirements.

The purchasing department is responsible for the commercial section of the specification. This portion of the specification is generally invariant for a given project unless a lowest evaluated bidder should take very firm exception to its provisions and the purchasing department should decide that an adjustment to the commercial conditions is in the project's interest. The commercial section may vary from project to project depending on the client's legal situation and practices.

In some cases, the client acts as the purchasing agent and may structure the project this way to keep fiscal control of the project. The engineer-architect serves as a design professional only. Contracts are written directly between the client and the vendors. This arrangement keeps the engineer-architect from any direct financial responsibility.

If the client prefers, the engineer-architect performs the purchasing. It may be that the client does not want to establish a sufficient staff to accept fiscal responsibility. If large construction projects are not often part of the client's business, assembling the necessary purchasing personnel for a short period is not good business.

If the engineer is the total project supplier, the engineer will grant the contracts and the engineer's purchasing department does the work. The current tendency is for the client to hold the engineer responsible for the total project. This approach shifts many risks from the client to the engineer.

If the project organization makes the engineer's firm responsible for costs on the project, the commercial section can be the engineer's standard and be invariant from project to project. Frequently, purchasing is a service provided to the client. In this case, the client has input into the commercial section, and it will vary from project to project. In any case, the specification writer should be aware of the commercial section as it affects his or her portion of the specification.

The purchasing department is responsible for trouble-free and economical procurement. It is also responsible for the procurement schedule. When the project was being planned, the purchasing department was presumably consulted on the lead time required. *Lead time* can be defined as the length of time between placing a purchase order and receiving the equipment. Lead time should be used to establish specification delivery date.

The purchasing department appears in the production process at the step of adding the commercial section. They may also review the specification to see if any of the technical provisions are likely to give rise to commercial problems. They will not review the specification from a technical point of view. Finally, the purchasing department will issue the specification to vendors with the invitation to bid, ending the production process.

It is the duty of purchasing department personnel to be knowledgeable about the commercial aspects of specifications. They are expected to know which vendors are reliable in the sense that they deliver equipment on time and in accordance with the specification. They negotiate contracts with the vendors. Like all other members of the specification team, they are expected to perform their work on schedule and within budget.

Word Processing Department

Managing the word processing function has an important effect on the success or failure of the specification production effort. Word processing itself is a purely mechanical function, presenting little technical difficulty. What distinguishes a successful word processing effort is good scheduling and attention to detail. Modern computer-based techniques make the effort much easier since it is so easy to make the changes demanded by the approval steps. It is no longer necessary to retype an entire document to make changes in it. It is necessary to keep the disks or tapes in order and easily retrievable. The engineers must now resist the temptation to recycle specifications through word processing more times than is necessary, since it is so easy. Excess churning of specifications can ruin scheduling. It is also an unnecessary expense.

The word processing manager must be, above all, calm and tactful. Many people try to use word processing to make up for their own inadequacies. If they are late, they try to use word processing to make up the time. Engineers also tend to deliver products that are borderline legible. Establishing a standard for legibility is a great exercise in tact, trying to satisfy both the engineer and the typist.

The Client

The client is all-important, since he or she pays the bills. The client is the ultimate judge of the success or failure of the production effort.

The privileges and duties of the client should be spelled out in the contract. A good client abides by the spirit of the contract.

Often, the client has the right to approve specifications as shown in Fig. 3-1. If the contract between the engineer and the client is well written, it will define what the·approval right means. If this contract is written on a fixed-price basis with a fixed schedule, approval rights can be of major importance. Delays in approval can ruin production schedules. Excessive changes in specifications caused by client comments can ruin both schedules and costs.

Sometimes client personnel try to modify contract requirements by withholding approval. This practice is disruptive and illegitimate. Both client and engineer-architect must insist that approval stay within established bounds and that contract modifications be made with due formality.

If the contract between the engineer and the client is on a cost-plus basis, approval rights are less important. The engineer is prepared to accept direction from the client by any means both parties agree to use.

No matter what the contractual provisions are, approval practices can disrupt the project schedule and budget.

Any specification submitted to the client for approval should be a finished product, ready for issue. Client preferences should have been determined and incorporated into the specification, and the specification should be in accordance with contract requirements. If all that is so, approval should be a formality.

Specification Production in the Manufacturing Industry

A discrete project in the manufacturing industry is subject to the basic principles and processes described above. If the project is manufacturing a specific product, such as a ship, the parallels are very close. If the project is an internal one, such as the development of a new product, the parallels are close, but some differences occur. Upper management can take the place of the client. Instead of being only tools to get the job done, specifications are part of the product. They will be used continually during the repeated manufacture of the new product.

Some manufacturers use administrative specifications to direct production in their own shops. In other cases, shop orders and shop drawings are used. The effect is the same. There is a document which states what must be done. We will, for the sake of convenience, call this document a specification. It will differ from a vendor specification since it has no accompanying commercial section. Also the shop, which stands in the place of the vendor, has a strong voice in the specification's development, since its costs and convenience are important to the success of the product.

A manufacturer will use vendor specifications to procure items he or she does not care to manufacture.

If the manufacturer is involved in the repetitive manufacture of a product, a given specification will be used over and over again. The project focus loses pertinence. Instead, emphasis will be placed on maintaining a library of specifications. They will be updated often to incorporate the lessons of procurement, the experience of production, or changes due to changing technology.

4
Proposal Evaluation Management

Definition of Proposal

A *proposal* is a vendor's response to a specification. Like a specification, it will have a technical section and a commercial section. In brief, a proposal is an offer to provide equipment or a service. It is rare that a proposal is completely responsive to a specification or that all proposals received in response to a specification are exactly comparable.

A contract between two parties must have a text the two parties agree to. It can be the specification or the proposal, either as modified to suit the agreement. A rare, but expensive, alternative, is to write a "confirmed specification" which is agreed to by both parties. Usually, the proposal is the surviving technical document. This is perceived as saving the engineer the trouble and expense of modifying the specification. The commercial part of the contract is more commonly based on the purchaser's standard wording.

A proposal can be a very simple document, say a single-page letter referencing a catalog page. It can also be a very complex document. A proposal for a large complete power plant can be a set of books occupying 3 feet of shelf space.

Proposal Evaluation

The proposals received in response to an inquiry must be evaluated and the vendor selected. The selection process can be a simple matter if the specification and proposal are simple. In Chap. 1 the example of a specification for a box of screws was cited as the simplest form of specification. The proposal would consist of the clerk showing you the box of screws (technical) and announcing the price (commercial). The corresponding evaluation would be to look at the box to verify that it was the right kind of screw and decide whether the price was fair.

On the other hand a complex proposal, especially in response to a vague specification, can cause a large evaluation effort. A recent case the author was involved in required a 1200 person-day effort by the consultant and at least as large an effort on the part of the client. Even larger proposal evaluation efforts have occurred.

Some forms of proposal require no, or almost no, evaluation effort. A commodity or catalog specification requires only checking to see that the proposal conforms to the specification and selection of the lowest price. The evaluation procedure can then be very informal.

Most evaluations are not that simple. They require a significant amount of review and verification of the data presented. They result in an evaluation report. This report is an administrative instrument. It leaves a record of why a vendor was selected, and it gives the project management, engineering management, and client a specific document to approve. The procedure for preparing the report provides the engineer and purchasing department with a structured approach to proposal evaluation, thus ensuring that they consider all aspects of the evaluation adequately. Evaluation reports take a significant person-day effort. Accordingly, they should be prepared only when necessary and then kept as simple as practical. A typical table of contents for an evaluation report is given in Table 4-1.

Table 4-1. Evaluation Report Outline

Part 1:   Comparison of proposals

  Bid prices

  Adjusted costs

  Evaluated costs

  Delivery

  Exceptions

  Technical features

Part 2:   Analysis of proposals

  Analysis of technical features

  Conformance to specification requirements

  Commercial analysis

Part 3:   Recommendation

  Results of analysis

  Vendor selection

  Contract price

An evaluation report is usually short, less than 10 pages. In the case of a large project where an especially good record is required, the report can easily be several hundred pages.

A flowchart for proposal evaluation is shown in Fig. 4-1. Like any flowchart in this book, it is typical. A basic assumption in this chart is

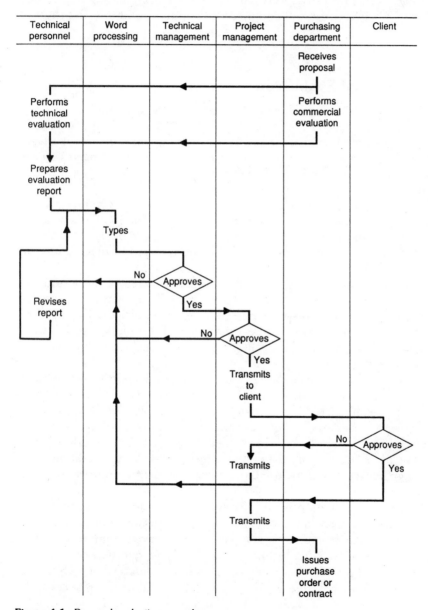

Figure 4-1. Proposal evaluation procedure

that the engineering department is responsible for preparing the evaluation report. Selection of the vendor is a joint responsibility between the engineering and purchasing departments. These responsibilities are frequently but not necessarily arranged this way. In one organization the author was associated with, the engineering department was asked to state which proposals were satisfactory. The purchasing department then evaluated price and commercial conditions and selected the vendor.

Commercial Evaluation

Since the purchasing department is responsible for relationships with vendors, they receive the proposal. A copy of the proposal is sent to the responsible engineer either directly or through the project manager. The project manager must know that the proposal has been received and is being evaluated, since he or she is responsible for project budget and schedule.

The purchasing department then proceeds with the commercial evaluation. The evaluation starts with a point-by-point comparison of the terms and conditions offered by the vendor with the purchasing department's standard. Differences are noted and resolved by negotiation with the vendor.

On a small or standard piece of equipment, review of terms and conditions can be perfunctory. The vendor is usually agreeable to accepting the purchaser's terms. On a large contract, and particularly in international trade, the review can be very involved. Resolution of questions such as which country's law will govern the contract and how disputes will be resolved can be very complex.

The commercial review often includes an evaluation of the vendors' financial health and consequent reliability. Also, the record of the vendors' past commercial performances is reviewed. Presumably, these factors were considered before placing the vendors on the bidders list. However, doubtful vendors are sometimes placed on the bidders list because of a paucity of acceptable alternatives. Also, conditions may change between the time the bidders list is prepared and proposals are received.

Economic evaluation is often considered technical, rather than commercial. This is particularly true where the specification permits proposals which are not directly comparable or where custom permits technical alternatives. When economics are a simple question of price and time value of money, they can be considered commercial or technical. If the question of risk due to the vendor's financial health is a consideration, economics becomes a commercial question. The possibility that the vendor takes a large part of the money and then either disappears or goes bankrupt without delivering the product is a commercial risk.

Technical Evaluation

Ideally, the technical evaluation would be prepared by the writer who wrote the specification. The writer knows the specification, including its intent, better than anyone else.

Although one engineer will do the bulk of the evaluation, help may be needed from others. If another discipline furnished a specification insert, that discipline should evaluate the portion of the proposal that relates to the insert. Specialist engineers will be called upon to evaluate sections where the responsible engineer's expertise is lacking.

The technical evaluation can be carried out in parallel with the commercial evaluation. The two aspects of evaluation can usually be considered independently, with a reconciliation as part of producing the final, consolidated report. Most commonly, the choice of vendor is made by the technical evaluation, with commercial considerations providing a veto. In this context, price is considered a technical factor.

The first step in a technical evaluation is a point-by-point comparison between specification requirements and features of the equipment offered. Any differences found must be evaluated. They can be accepted, if considered unimportant or satisfactory, or the vendor can be asked to modify the proposal to conform to specification requirements. A large number of exceptions deemed satisfactory is a mark of an overly restrictive, low-quality specification. A large number of exceptions requiring adjustment is a mark of a poorly prepared proposal.

The review should then consider items in the proposal not required by the specification. They are evaluated in the same manner as items covered by the specification.

Economic Evaluation

The economic evaluation will consider not only the price, but the time value of money. The usual technique for evaluating this factor is the present-worth method. If a payment is required at some time in the future, the amount of money that must be set aside now to meet this payment is computed. The required amount is less than the payment because the money accumulates interest until it is needed. This factor is not important with simple equipment that has a short delivery time with a single payment due on delivery. It is important, though, in cases where progress payments are made periodically over a long term of the project.

Another economic factor which must be taken into account in long-term projects is the anticipated course of inflation. Often, instead of offering a fixed price, vendors will quote a price as a base price, valid today, plus an adjustment based on indices such as the cost-of-living index. The evaluation must include an analysis of which vendor's price adjustment procedure is most favorable to the buyer.

Specifications and Evaluations

In a well-organized specification effort, evaluation has been considered in preparing the specification. Much time can be saved in the evaluation by using the right provisions in the specification. Vendors should be told whether alternative proposals will be considered or whether they will be held strictly to the specification provisions. If price will be the sole criterion, vendors should be told that. Sometimes the client will have opinions on the state of technology. Sometimes the latest technology is desired, in spite of the possibility that untried technology may develop problems. Other clients, more conservative, will want proven technology to improve reliability. These attitudes should be specified to ensure responsive proposals.

It is good practice to have the evaluation criteria stated explicitly in the specification.

Types of Evaluations

Evaluation procedures take various forms, depending on the practices of the evaluating organization and the amount of scrutiny the decision will have to stand.

Governmental organizations tend to have the most rigid evaluation procedures. Since it is the public's money, governmental evaluations have to be well documented and be fair to both the bidders and the buyer. The record must show that no bidder has benefited from a private relationship with the evaluator or from information that was not available to competitors. It must show that the entire procurement process, from specification writing on, was motivated by the public's interest, rather than the interests of public employees, their consultants, or the bidders.

For these reasons, government specifications tend to be public documents, available to all. Invitations to bid are often published in newspapers, leaving a public record of the event and permitting any alert and qualified member of the public to bid. Bid openings tend to be public events so that any member of the public can know who submitted a bid and how much it was.

The specifications tend to be very precise so that the buyer can get what he or she wants even though the successful bidder is someone unknown prior to the bid submittal. Alternative bids are severely restricted, if permitted at all. Usually, a base bid in accordance with the specification is usually required even if the bidder chooses to submit an alternative proposal.

In a government bid, contact between the evaluator and the bidders is often prohibited after bid submittal. If contact is permitted, the subject of discussion is usually limited to clarification of the proposal, rather than modifications to it. A record of the discussions is maintained. Ideally, evaluation of a proposal in a government procurement is limited to verifying that the proposal is in accordance with the specification and then selecting the bidder with the lowest evaluated price. Then the evaluation report must show that this has been done in an objective and fair manner.

In a commercial environment, the entire evaluation process can be freer. If the evaluator is an engineering firm and the purchaser is a publicly regulated utility, the degree of freedom is not great. Maximum freedom exists when the evaluator is working for his or her own account. The evaluator is then responsible only to his or her own management. Then procedures are limited only by the evaluator's goals and ethics and the reputation he or she wants to maintain with potential vendors. In this case, the evaluator is free to ask for modifications to a proposal, including price, during the evaluation. Such requests are an attempt to get the best equipment at the best price. The disadvantage of using such a procedure is that the vendors will not initially submit their best proposal or their best price. The best vendors may not submit a proposal at all, considering the trouble of negotiations not worth their time. The entire evaluation process becomes more time-consuming because of the negotiations.

The simplest evaluation procedure results from a clear, precise specification, acceptance of the prices as submitted, and the absence of a requirement for documentation.

5
Purchase Document Preparation

General

Previously, a distinction has been drawn between the technical specification and the commercial part of the complete purchase document. This book is primarily concerned with the technical specification. For a complete account of the procurement process, the reader should consult works such as Ref. 1. In this book, some time must be spent discussing the commercial section since it affects the technical specification. A general understanding of commercial matters is necessary to write an adequate specification. It is necessary at this point to describe a step in the specification cycle which is basically commercial.

The previous chapter concerned evaluation. At the conclusion of the evaluation, a vendor had been selected and technical and commercial agreement had been reached on all features of the equipment or services. It is now time to consummate the purchase.

Contracts

A contract is an agreement between two or more parties. It can be more narrowly defined as a binding agreement based on the genuine assent of the parties, made for a lawful object, between competent parties, in the form required by law, and generally supported by consideration. Oral contracts can be legal, but they are not a good practice because of the possibilities for misunderstandings and imperfect recollection. A contract should be a written document. Each party should have a copy of the contract with all the pertinent signatures.

The technical specification may be a part of the contract. If so, it is the valid expression of the agreement between the vendor and the purchaser. Any differences between the specification and the proposal must be reconciled, and the resulting agreement included in the specification. To do otherwise will, at a minimum, lead to misunderstandings and could lead to lawsuits which disturb the project schedule and cost money.

An alternate to making the technical specification part of the contract is to make the technical proposal part of the contract. In this case it must be modified to fit the agreement. Generally, this is easier than modifying the specification. Engineers like this arrangement because it is usually less work for them. Vendors usually like this arrangement because they are more confident that they understand what is required of them.

On nuclear projects, the specification must be the surviving document for quality-control reasons. The record must show an unbroken chain of logic from project nuclear safety requirements to equipment features.

The purchasing department will prepare the contract. A partial review is required by the specification engineer to ensure that the contract carries out his or her intent.

Finally, the contract will be signed for the purchaser by an authorized member of the purchasing department, usually the manager, and by an authorized representative of the vendor.

Purchase Orders

A purchase order is a form sent to the vendor by the purchaser. An example of the face side of a purchase order is shown in Fig. 5-1. The reverse side of the purchase order, not reproduced here, usually contains commercial terms and conditions pertaining to the order. The major difference between a purchase order and a contract is that a purchase order is unilateral at the time it is issued. A purchase order cannot logically be written without such complete information that the vendor can accept it without modification. This information includes a price. This might be a catalog price or one determined by a previous negotiation, perhaps by telephone.

Most purchase orders are made with multiple carbon copies. Most of the copies are used within the originating organization. One copy may be an acknowledgment copy. If the vendor signs this copy without com-

PURCHASE ORDER

APPLIED POWER ASSOCIATES 10810 Farnam Drive Omaha, NE. 68154 phone: (402) 334-9333	**P.O. NO.** №̲ 20328 ◁ This number must appear on all correspondence, invoices, and shipping papers

P.O. NO. №̲ 20328

DATE OF ORDER May 19, 1988 CALLED IN

REQUISITION NO./DEPT ERP   CHG. 5.04

DATE WANTED ASAP

┌   ┐
TO FISHER SCIENTIFIC

                        VCN 101

  JERRY
└   ┘

TERMS

F.O.B.

SHIP VIA UPS

SHIP TO

QUANTITY	DESCRIPTION	UNIT PRICE	AMOUNT
4 EA.	#14-809-66 ACETAL UNWIRE TEST TUBE RACKS	$9.50	
3 PKS	#14-932F BARO SILICA TEST TUBES WITH CAPS 25 X 200 ML 48/PK	61.92	
	RECEIVED BY: _____ DATE: _____		

Please acknowledge receipt of order and advise exact shipping date.   BY: _____

AUTHORIZED SIGNATURE

Figure 5-1. Example of the face side of a purchase order

ment and returns it to the originating organization, a contract has been formed. Also, if the vendor takes action that indicates acceptance of the purchase order, such as shipping the specified material, a contract is formed.

A purchase order is commonly used with a commodity specification or a catalog specification. The technical information from the specification can be transcribed on the purchase order. A more complex specification could be used by referring to it on the form and attaching the specification. This is not ordinarily done, since there is a chance the vendor will have exceptions to the specification and since the vendor usually cannot quote a fixed price until the specification is reviewed.

Simple purchase order forms can be purchased at business supply stores. They will suffice for many purposes. Such order forms do not ordinarily have commercial terms and conditions written on them. An established business will ordinarily have its own purchase order forms with commercial terms and conditions printed on the back. By shipping the commodity requested or signing the acknowledgment copy, the vendor implicitly accepts the terms and conditions. The purchasing department will prepare and issue the purchase order.

References

1. Aljian, George W. (editor in chief), *Purchasing Handbook,* McGraw-Hill, New York, 1977.

6

Specification Enforcement Management

General

A specification that cannot be enforced is worthless. The main object of writing a specification is to acquire the right equipment or service economically. The specification must therefore contain all the requirements necessary to ensure that the vendor delivers equipment that meets specification requirements. In addition to stating the technical requirements, the specification must provide a mechanism for ensuring that the equipment, when delivered, actually includes those requirements. Not all these mechanisms are in the technical part of the procurement document. Having the right commercial requirements, such as a performance bond or retaining a part of the payment until the equipment is accepted, is a powerful help.

In many cases, the vendor, represented by salespeople, is very agreeable until the order is placed. Thereafter, a state of tension exists, with the vendor trying to fill the order as economically as practical and the buyer trying to get the equipment in accordance with needed requirements. The vendor may also be trying to get extra payment for items which were not clearly specified but which the buyer might need. Even the schedule may be an item of controversy. The vendor may use delay as an inducement to get the buyer to relax technical requirements. Also, the vendor may use delay to avoid the use of overtime or to find time to placate other, more insistent, customers.

There are few absolutes in specification enforcement. The ultimate weapon is a lawsuit, but this weapon is useful only to get monetary recompense after the project is over. It will very seldom assist in getting good-quality equipment or getting it on schedule. More useful techniques are persuading the vendor that it is less trouble to obey the specification than not to, persuading the vendor that adhering to the specification is in the vendor's long-term business interest, or using moral force. Withholding payment is also an inducement, provided the amount withheld is sufficiently large. The usual amount, 5 to 10 percent of the price, is sometimes ineffective.

Because there are few absolutes in specification enforcement, the purchaser's reputation is important. A purchaser who gives up specification requirements when little pressure is applied will have much trouble in enforcing the specification. A purchaser who is adamant, obstinate, and unreasonable will have less overt trouble but might get higher prices to make up for the vendor's extra trouble. Probably the ideal reputation to have is one of standing up for your rights as a normal practice but not insisting on having your way when it is unreasonable.

Establishing one's reputation starts with specification provisions. The specification should contain all the necessary requirements but no unnecessary ones. Once the specifier withdraws unnecessary requirements, it becomes harder to enforce the really necessary ones.

Consistent specification enforcement is also important. If vendors find they can sometimes get concessions easily, they will try harder to get them, leading to a lot of unnecessary interaction. The project manager should ensure that enforcement is uniform and consistent.

Ultimately, the client establishes the project's reputation. If vendors find that the client will give concessions that the engineer will not, they will try that route consistently. If the client does not want to enforce the specifications, the engineer cannot.

Information Submission

Most specifications will have a provision requiring submittal of specific information, predominantly drawings. Such submittal may be a means for the engineer to obtain information needed to complete the design of the project, or it may be a means of enforcing the specification. Whatever the motive for requiring the submittal, a complex project will involve submittal of a large amount of vendor information. The specifications will have to include standardized provisions for the orderly flow of this information.

The specification writer does not have complete freedom with regard to requesting information. Requiring too much information will increase the writer's costs because of the time required to handle drawings and will increase vendor costs because of the expense of creating and sending the information. These costs will ultimately be borne by the project owner. On the other hand, the engineer must require enough information to do the work and to fulfill all obligations to the owner.

Each industry has its own practices with regard to drawing submittal. Departing from these practices should be done with forethought, since at a minimum such departures create confusion. They may also create legal problems. For example, in the building industry, structural engineers have a duty to ensure that structural details developed by the steel fabricator carry out the engineer's design intent. They carry out this duty by reviewing detail drawings submitted by the fabricator.

A flow diagram for the vendor drawing review process is shown in Fig. 6-1. As usual, this is a generalized procedure. Unlike the previous diagrams, this one must accommodate a variety of possibilities.

Drawings may be submitted for approval. This procedure is used for specification enforcement. The usual specification will state that fabrication is not to start without an approved drawing. Drawing approval is used where the vendor must interpret specification requirements, and information showing the vendor's interpretation is not available at the time of the proposal. It is also used where the information on a drawing is crucial to completing the engineer's work, and the engineer is concerned that the vendor's choice of design might make the work more difficult.

Drawings may also be submitted for information. This procedure is ordinarily not used for enforcement. It is used to secure information needed for the engineer to complete the work but is not so crucial that approval is necessary. Information submittal is also used to secure information needed by the owner to operate and maintain the equipment.

Drawing approval is usually signified by a stamp applied to the drawing. The stamp serves as an obvious identification of the edition of the drawing which has been approved and is to be used for the project. A rejection stamp is applied to drawings which have been returned to the vendor for correction. A "for information only" stamp is applied to drawings reviewed for that purpose. Examples of these stamps are shown in Fig. 6-2.

A strong, well-organized plan file department, manned by competent clerks, is essential to the success of a complex project. A large project involves the use of several thousand drawings. Some are valid; some are not. The engineers and designers must be able to find and use the valid edition of each drawing when needed. It is also essential to the specification enforcement effort to know which of the required drawings have been received and approved. Vendors will often delay on submittal of

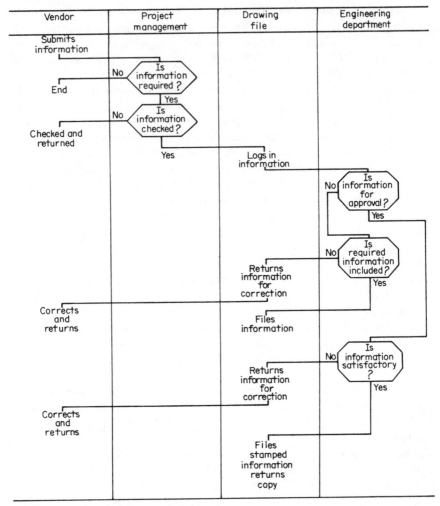

Figure 6-1. Vendor information procedure

drawings, either to save money or in the hope that a late review will be a cursory review.

The specification engineer should maintain a checklist and determine that all required drawings have been submitted on schedule and approved. If drawings are late, the engineer should have the vendor urged to submit the drawings. It is particularly difficult to persuade a vendor to resubmit a drawing once rejected. The project manager is responsible for making sure that the approval process is carried out for

```
┌─────────────────────────────┐   ┌─────────────────────────────┐
│          APPROVED           │   │  RETURNED FOR CORRECTION AND│
│     FOR ARRANGEMENT ONLY    │   │     ADDITIONAL INFORMATION  │
│   PROCEED WITH FABRICATION  │   │ DO NOT PROCEED WITH FABRICATION│
│   SUBJECT TO COMPLIANCE WITH│   │   SUBJECT TO COMPLIANCE WITH│
│   ALL CONTRACT REQUIREMENTS,│   │   ALL CONTRACT REQUIREMENTS,│
│  DRAWINGS, AND SPECIFICATIONS.│ │  DRAWINGS, AND SPECIFICATIONS.│
│                             │   │                             │
│                             │   │                             │
│  APPLIED POWER ASSOCIATES, INC.│ │ APPLIED POWER ASSOCIATES, INC.│
│     ENGINEERS-DESIGNERS     │   │     ENGINEERS-DESIGNERS     │
│                             │   │                             │
│         OMAHA, NE           │   │         OMAHA, NE           │
└─────────────────────────────┘   └─────────────────────────────┘

          ┌─────────────────────────────┐
          │      FOR INFORMATION        │
          │           ONLY              │
          │    SUBJECT TO COMPLIANCE WITH│
          │    ALL CONTRACT REQUIREMENTS,│
          │   DRAWINGS, AND SPECIFICATIONS.│
          │                             │
          │                             │
          │  APPLIED POWER ASSOCIATES, INC.│
          │     ENGINEERS-DESIGNERS     │
          │                             │
          │         OMAHA, NE           │
          └─────────────────────────────┘
```

Figure 6-2. Vendor drawing stamps

the project and is usually expected to handle communications with the vendors.

Inspection

Inspection is a fundamental means for enforcing a specification. Inspection means actually looking at the equipment being furnished or installed and verifying that it does truly meet the specification.

An inspector is a specialized and trained individual who must be able to understand the specification and to determine whether it is met.

Generally, it is not the inspector's duty to pass on the wisdom or importance of specification requirements, only to determine whether the
specification has been met and accordingly pass or reject the equipment. Modifications to specification requirements should be made by
the specifying engineer.

An inspector should be especially competent at quality-control procedures, since he or she will often be expected to accept the results of such
tests. In the mechanical area, for example, the inspector may be called
on to accept radiographs, which are particularly subject to interpretation. There are programs, such as that of the American Society for
Quality Control, for certification of inspectors.

Inspections can be specified at various stages in the production cycle.
The usual ones are

"Hold" points during fabrication

Performance tests

Shipping

Receiving

Installation

Hold point inspections are used when the work may be uninspectable
later or when a significant cost is about to be incurred. An example is
inspection of a drain pipe where it will be later covered with concrete.
Another type of hold point occurs when a test does not leave an adequate record to be reviewed later. An example of such a test is magnetic
particle testing, where the only verification is seeing the indication or its
absence. Hold points must be stated in the specification with a provision
that the inspector be informed adequately ahead of time so that he or
she can get to the inspection location without delaying the project.

Performance tests occur when the equipment has been assembled and
is close to shipment. They are often witnessed by the specifying engineer, since the engineer understands the performance requirements.
Again, adequate warning must be specified so that the engineer can get
to the test on time. The specification should state what happens if the
performance requirements are not met. The performance test occurs
late in the project. There is often not enough time to start over, so some
accommodation must be made to permit use of the tested performance.
In some cases, a minor departure from the performance requirements
can be covered by a penalty.

Shipping inspections are often specified, since the equipment can be
completely inspected at this time and since payment is often due upon
shipment. It is also much easier to change equipment that does not meet

specification requirements prior to shipment. On the other hand, shipment occurs late in the project schedule. If something is wrong with the equipment, it is often difficult to find the time to fix it.

Receiving inspections are often specified, since it is cheaper to inspect an item at the job site, rather than send an inspector to the factory. This is usually satisfactory for small items. The disadvantage to receiving inspections is that, if the item is unsatisfactory, arrangements must be made to return it. It also occurs even later in the project than other types of inspection.

Installation inspections are used mostly for erection activities. The owner will have inspectors on site to see that on-site work is performed properly. The specification will have to ensure that the erector cooperates in the inspections by allowing access to the work and inspection records. It will also have to specify the testing which must be conducted.

Engineer's Conferences

If a specification has a complex object, such as a complete water treatment system, engineer's conferences may be used to enforce the specification. Such a conference may be held either at the manufacturer's plant or at the engineer's location. The specification should state the number of conferences to be held, their location, and time. Time might be specified by a point in the production process, rather than by calendar time.

Engineer's conferences serve two major purposes. First, they check whether the project is on schedule. Second, they determine whether the vendor has interpreted the specification correctly and in fact intends to deliver a system in accordance with it.

An engineer's conference is an expensive technique. It is therefore used sparingly.

Use of Codes with Enforcement Provisions

Some codes include enforcement provisions. The prime example is the ASME Boiler and Pressure Vessel Code. This code is mandated by law in several states and by federal regulation in the nuclear industry, so it is especially important to specify the use of this code where applicable. Compliance with the code is indicated by an ASME inspector's stamp applied to the vessel and by supporting documentation. Existence of the stamp and supporting documentation should be verified at the shipping inspection or the receiving inspection.

A similar situation exists with regard to Underwriters' Laboratories. This organization tests electrical equipment and certifies it as safe. Existence of the certificate should be verified if the equipment is important. Since much of the equipment covered by Underwriters' Laboratories is small, such as light switches, the existence of an Underwriters' Laboratories label is sufficient to determine acceptance. Underwriters' Laboratories does not test each piece of equipment, but only each model.

PART 2
Techniques

7
Specification Scope

General

The foundation of almost all procurement actions is a contract. The only significant exception to this rule is procurement by an unacknowledged purchase order, where the supplier sends the material and an invoice without formal agreement. Obviously, this procedure is used only for small, well-defined procurement actions.

A contract is an agreement between two or more parties. In a procurement action, two parties are usually involved, that is, the vendor and the purchaser. It follows then, that a specification will be used as part of a contract and will be used in one procurement action with one vendor. Ideally, the specification should be tailored to fit the one procurement action.

As in many fundamental rules, there are reasons to bend or break this one in rare cases. One such case is the use of standard specifications with attached data sheets to fit the individual project. At the time a standard specification is written, a reasonable idea of the likely procurement actions is known from experience, but, obviously, the individual circumstances are not. It is thus possible that there might be some material in the standard specification which is extraneous to a particular procurement. This situation is acceptable if kept within reasonable bounds. Any extraneous material masks the real requirements and thus reduces clarity.

The probable procurement actions a specification will be used for should be the major factor in planning its scope. In most actions, then, a standard specification should contain little extraneous information. This principle implies a large number of relatively narrow standard specifications.

It is usually difficult to get authorization to write standard specifications since this is an overhead function which brings in no direct revenue. Organizations are therefore tempted to get the greatest coverage possible from their standard specifications by writing a few broad ones. This temptation should be avoided if practical, since it leads to confusion during procurement. In planning a standard specification effort, maximum use should be made of common sections to reduce preparation work. With modern word processing computer programs, it is possible to transfer blocks of words from specification to specification with a minimum of effort, making it easy to develop a group of narrow specifications suitable for individual procurement actions.

Standard specifications are not necessarily developed in-house. One can use standard specifications developed by organizations such as the Construction Specifications Institute provided one makes the necessary arrangements to do so. Copyright permission, for example, may have to be arranged. One can also use government specifications such as federal specifications or military specifications. All three will be familiar to suppliers in some fields. Construction Specification Institute specifications will be relevant to commercial work. One must be cautious in using them to be sure that the scope accurately describes what is required in the procurement action at hand. Federal and military specifications are usually too elaborate for commercial and industrial use but may be applicable in some cases.

Sometimes specifications for equipment groups are scoped so that the buyer can purchase the entire lot from one vendor or, instead, buy individual items from various vendors. The motive is maximum economy. In this case, the instructions to bidders must ask for a price on the entire lot and a price on each item. Finding the combination that gives the lowest cost and is technically satisfactory is then a part of the evaluation. One must realize that buying from several vendors increases contract administration and inspection costs. Also, maintenance and operating crews must then cope with equipment from many vendors. These problems may be acceptable.

In this case also, procurement action is by a contract with each vendor containing a specification which applies to that vendor. Unless the specification is appropriately rewritten, it may also contain some extraneous material intended for other vendors.

Wholesale versus Retail

Customers have a choice of buying directly from a manufacturer, from a wholesaler, or from a retailer. Even the smallest of projects will use a combination. For example, when building a $10,000 solar energy system, the author's firm bought the pump from a manufacturer, instrumentation from a wholesaler, and tube fittings from a retailer.

Manufacturers give the best price but maintain little stock in inventory, so their delivery times are comparatively long. Dealing with them also tends to require more administrative time. Finally, they may simply refuse to deal in small quantities.

Retailers are constituted for instant response, often over the counter. They are informal and work with purchase orders, by periodically billing a running account, or by cash. Their prices tend to be high since they deal in small amounts and must maintain a large inventory.

Wholesalers are in an intermediate position. They want to deal with retailers or large commercial or industrial customers.

There are advantages in dealing with each level of vendor. Manufacturers give the lowest price and are accustomed to responding to detailed specifications. They are organized to work with large, discrete procurement actions. They are more flexible than wholesalers and retailers in tailoring equipment to fit the customer's needs. By enforcement of a specification with a manufacturer, the customer can maintain control over equipment features and quality.

A wholesaler may deal with several manufacturers and can therefore accept a broader specification than any one manufacturer. A wholesaler might be able to accept a specification for all valves or all circuit breakers on a given project. Some wholesalers can accept a detailed specification by relaying the requirements to manufacturers they deal with. The customer's alternative to a wholesaler is to order, say, all butterfly valves from one manufacturer, all globe and gate valves from another manufacturer, and so on. This procedure results in considerable administrative cost. The wholesaler can often perform this administration more efficiently than the engineer or customer, since the wholesaler has continual contact with the manufacturers as part of everyday business. It is also easier to add unforeseen valves to the order as construction progresses, since the wholesaler is organized to accept such changes.

A retailer can provide a quick response for items in stock but ordinarily will have nothing to do with detailed specifications or inspections. About the best one can hope for, if the item is not in stock, is that the retailer will order it in accordance with a catalog specification.

Including Equipment in
Contractor's Scope

The erector, usually called a contractor, is the organization that actually puts the project, whether a building, factory, process plant, or power plant, together, at the site. On a given project there may be a general contractor in charge of all work at the site, or there may be several contractors — substructure, superstructure, mechanical, electrical, instrumentation, and so on. In the former case, there may be specialist subcontractors with the work being coordinated by the general contractor. In the latter case, the owner must appoint a construction manager to coordinate the work.

A general contractor will accept complete scheduling responsibility and give a fixed price for the work, assuming that the specification can be written clearly enough to make that procedure feasible. If there are several contractors, they can each accept the same kind of responsibility for their work. Their overall responsibility is weakened since the work of each is impacted by the work of the others and by the project manager's actions. For example, the electrical contractor cannot start to work until the structural contractor has erected the building in which electrical work is to be done. Therefore, the electrical contractor's schedule is only as good as the structural contractor's performance permits.

If a contractor accepts schedule responsibility, that contractor has the right to expect other organizations under contract to the owner (contractors and vendors) to perform on schedule. If the engineer or owner procures equipment independently of the contractor, the equipment must arrive on schedule, or the contractor has the right to claim delay and additional cost. It must also be the kind of equipment the contractor had planned on. If, for example, the electrical contractor had been led to expect a distributed control system with signals conveyed to the control room via a small number of data highways, the contractor has the right to consider the schedule and cost impacted if instead an older type of control system where each instrument is wired to the control room is furnished. To remove these problems, supply of equipment is often included in the contractor's scope, and the specifications are scoped accordingly.

On the other hand, if the owner or the engineer procures the equipment directly, control over equipment quality and features is strengthened. On many projects, a combination is used, with the owner procuring vital and sophisticated equipment directly. The contractor procures standard items and small items such as reinforcing bar, small pipe, fittings and valves, and electrical conduit, all of which are needed in quantity. Delays in obtaining these items can impact the schedule severely. The contractor must then include the cost of this procurement in the fee. It is usually wise to accept this cost, since the contractor is efficient at this activity and since it reduces the contractor's claims for delays. If this cost were not in the contractor's fee, it would be in the owner's direct cost. The contractor can probably perform the service more economically.

Systems versus Components

Many items are bought as systems. One example is water treatment systems, which are usually bought from specialist firms. These firms accept responsibility for producing water of a specified quantity and quality, using water of a given quality as input. Most engineering firms can, in principle, design their own water treatment systems. They usually choose to delegate this task since the specialists are more efficient at it and because there will be cost resistance to including this service in the engineer's scope.

The usual considerations of control enter into this case also. Either one must have a detailed specification or one must deal with vendors of known quality and good will.

A question which arises in system procurement is system reliability. Reliability can be enhanced by better-quality equipment or by redundant equipment. *Redundant equipment* can be defined as equipment beyond that required for the system to furnish its function at rated output. An example of redundant equipment would be a spare pump, to be used if the one required for the system is out of service. Such redundancy must be specified if it is to be obtained. It will increase cost.

System design specifications must address several other factors such as quality of equipment, control systems including compatibility with the rest of the plant control system, layout for ease of maintenance, available space, and so on. Many of these items would be under the engineer's control if components, rather than systems, were specified. Many of them, such as space available, would not ordinarily appear explicitly in component specifications.

A simple system performance specification will not usually be sufficient unless the possible vendors are limited to those which are known to be trustworthy and unless enough information is provided in the proposal to judge the quality of the system in detail.

In many cases, system specification gives good results. The decision whether to specify systems or components depends on practices in the particular industry and the availability of suitable vendors.

Battery Limits

The scope of every specification must have its physical limits. To take the simple case of a horizontal centrifugal pump, the usual scope of supply includes the pump itself, the drive motor, the coupling connecting them, and the base plate. Sometimes, though, the customer will want the motor removed from the scope so that all motors for the project can be supplied from a single source. In this case, the specification must include such items as whether the pump manufacturer supplies the coupling or a base plate that accommodates both the pump and the motor. Similarly, all other physical limits of the pump must be specified in the specification, or the instructions to bidders must require this information in the proposal.

The above paragraph emphasized what is to be included in the supplier's scope. When properly specified, the result is to require everything within specified limits to be supplied. Ideally, the complete project can be assembled from the packages so specified. The limits of the packages should be specified so that this is possible.

Limits of supply are often known as *battery limits*. A system specification may have complex battery limits. Properly, each pipe and cable attached to the system should have its connection point and size specified. Each commodity entering or leaving the system, such as electric current and voltage or cooling water quantity pressure and temperature, should be specified. Each load delivered to the supporting structure should be specified. The less important information can be left to be supplied by the vendor while carrying out the contract, rather than being specified at the beginning.

Battery limits are particularly important in large international projects, where the complete project can be made up of interconnected systems, sometimes called islands, furnished by vendors from several different countries.

Furnish versus Furnish and Erect

Systems can be furnished as equipment, or they can be furnished and erected. In the latter case, responsibility is consolidated. The vendor must have erection capability at the site, either by the vendor's own forces or by subcontract.

Furnish and erect can be very effective where the project can be divided into several islands with geographic separation. It is difficult if the various system vendors must work in the same space, but this procedure is sometimes used anyway.

On international projects, furnish and erect can be impossible, since the vendor does not have access to labor where the project is being erected.

Work by Others

One means of clarifying the scope of a specification is by including a section with this title. Let us assume that a specification requires a vendor to furnish a system. It will clarify the vendor's scope if the Work by Others section includes system erection and test.

This section should contain only material pertinent to the specification at hand, since a specification is a means for communication with the vendor and extraneous material can only serve to confuse and obscure. Some specification writers use this section to remind themselves of information to be included in other specifications.

Occasionally, a vendor has a direct interest in work by others. A system vendor may be required to furnish a system and guarantee its performance. Erection and test might then be done by others. The system vendor will want to ensure that the test is fair and adequate for the guarantees and may need the right and duty to review test procedure prepared by others.

Other Limits

Table 7-1 lists other supply limits. The location of delivery can be especially important for international projects. Unless otherwise specified, title passes, i.e., equipment becomes the property of the owner, when the equipment is loaded on the transportation at the factory. This ar-

Table 7-1. Supply Limits

1. Physical limits
2. Shipment — passage of title and responsibility
3. Packaging
4. Erection
5. Tests at site
6. Instruction manuals
7. Operation manuals
8. Drawings
9. Erection specifications
10. Erection supervision
11. Start-up supervision
12. Construction spares
13. Maintenance spares
14. Material certificates
15. Code certificates
16. Training

rangement is designated FOB (free on board). Any damage to the equipment from this point on is the responsibility of the shipper, not the vendor. Any insurance costs are borne by the new owner. If any part of the shipping is to be borne by the vendor, it must be so specified.

Sometimes an international customer will want shipment to a seaport in the vendor's scope. This arrangement is known as FOB vessel (vessel may be named) port of export. In this way, the customer does not need to cope with transportation in a foreign country but can choose the sea transportation method. The customer can then also choose the mode of transportation in his or her own country.

Packaging may be specified. Domestically, and on a project with good warehousing, packaging may not be important except for especially delicate equipment. It is more necessary to consider packaging for international projects. It is most necessary for remote and tropical projects where good warehousing may not be available and protection during shipment might be necessary.

Documentation (e.g., operating manuals) is not a physical part of equipment, but it is certainly important. It may be assumed that some, the manufacturer's standard, will be supplied. Even consumer goods come with an installation manual and an operating manual. If anything more is desired, it must be specified. Installation drawings are often a necessity, and, for complex items, erection specifications. Code certificates are often legally required.

Material certificates may be required to ensure that one gets what one specified. It is difficult to inspect in the field for some differences in materials. For example, distinguishing between types 304 and 316 stainless steel is very difficult without using destructive methods. Fake material certificates are not completely unknown, but requiring certificates reduces mislabeling.

Any services required from the vendor have to be included in the scope. Often, a very complex piece of equipment such as a large steam generator will require an on-site erection advisor and possibly manufacturer's representatives during start-up and test. These services often cannot be firmly priced in the proposal since the time required cannot be defined, but at least a rate can be established and a commitment that the service will be available can be obtained.

Spare parts should be included in the scope as much as possible. It is usually difficult to describe what parts are required in the initial specification, since equipment details are not known. Also, maintenance personnel will want a voice in the selection of spare parts, based on their review of the maintenance manuals. Often, a specification calls for a list and prices of spare parts to be in the proposal. Actual selection of the spares is then deferred.

Construction spares are often included in the scope to make up for damage and pilferage during construction. Such spares are usually small, complete equipment such as small valves, circuit breakers, and switches.

Warranties and Guarantees

These two terms are similar in many ways. Either is a promise to pay in case of a fault in equipment or a service. For specifications, the term warranty is preferred. Engineers are mostly concerned with performance and schedule warranties.

Ordinarily, it can be assumed that a specification will be met. Compliance can be confirmed by inspection, and the material can be rejected if it does not comply. Payment can be withheld until the fault is made good.

Occasionally, the remedy of complete rejection can be draconian. This is particularly true of performance such as efficiency, capacity, and reliability. It may be impossible to measure these parameters until the equipment has been installed, tested, and sometimes operated for a period of time. Consider the case, for example, of a circulating water pump. This equipment is necessary to plant performance and difficult to replace. Large circulating water pumps are also difficult to test in a shop, since such a test requires a special pump suction pit and an enormous amount of water. If on test in the completed plant the efficiency is found to be 84 percent instead of the specified or proposed 85 percent, it is too late to reject the equipment. However, the customer has suffered an economic loss. The proper remedy is a payment proportional to the deficiency in efficiency.

Warranties provide for such payment, with a target parameter (e.g., efficiency = 85 percent), a penalty for failure to meet the parameter, and a bonus for exceeding it. The bonus is required for legal reasons. Warranties are a useful device when properly formulated and included in the specification scope before ordering the equipment. Performance warranties require explicit definition and test procedures for determining whether the warranty has been met.

Warranties can also be used for schedules. In this case, a penalty is specified for each day's delay in a given event, and a bonus for each day early. The warranty clause must be written so that the date of the event is within the vendor's control. If prior action is required from others, it must be assured that the schedule for the prior action is met. Otherwise, the warranty is void. Any schedule warranty will have a provision for force majeure, that is, major events the vendor cannot foresee or control, like tornadoes and civil disturbances.

Scope Precautions

A legal principle that applies to specifications is that "whatever is not included is excluded." It is more correct to cover an area with a general statement than with a detailed list that may later prove to be partial. For example, it is more restrictive to say "the equipment shall be in accordance with the ASME Code" than to say "the equipment shall be designed and fabricated in accordance with the ASME Code." If one uses the latter wording, the equipment might not get an ASME stamp, since certification in accordance with the code was not asked for. The former wording at least gives the equipment a clear legal right to the stamp.

It is important to be sure that a specification is commercially feasible. One particular person who specified a compressor by catalog number and material (stainless steel) found that the compressor was available in many materials, but stainless steel was not one of them. This compressor was part of a large lot of material procured through a contractor. The contractor accepted the contract and later informed the purchaser that the compressor could not be supplied since it was improperly specified. The purchaser had to pay a premium to get a satisfactory compressor in time to meet the project schedule.

The scope of all specifications should be reviewed to ensure that everything needed for the project is covered someplace. Late discovery of omissions causes delays and payment of premium costs to get equipment quickly.

Assignment of risk is a consideration in determining specification scope. Risks are always present: risk that inflation will occur, risk that regulatory agencies will not issue permits, risks that subsoil conditions are not as expected, and so on.

There are two principles that can be applied. First, if one party can minimize the risk, it should be in that party's scope. For example, if the customer is a municipality, the customer should assume the risk that building permits will not be issued on time. On the other hand, if the customer is a private entity and the vendor is expert at obtaining permits, the risk that a permit may be difficult to obtain should be in the vendor's scope.

Second, if the risk is undeterminable, it should generally be assumed by the customer. An example of such a risk is subsoil conditions at a site. If a contractor is asked to assume such a risk, the contractor will generally set the price high enough that money will not be lost even in the worst foreseeable case. If subsoil conditions are better than foreseen, the contractor will make a great deal of money and the customer has paid for the bad soil conditions. On the other hand, if the customer assumes the risk of bad soil conditions, competitive pressure will ensure that contractors set their price on the assumption that soil conditions are good. If they truly are good, the customer has saved a great deal of money.

Sometimes an overriding concern in risk assignment is the attitude of financiers. They like to minimize their risk. It may be easier to sell bonds if the constructor is willing to take the risk, even if the project costs more as a result.

Engineering and Architectural Contracts

The scope of these contracts must be considered as carefully as those in any other category. In the past, such contracts have been conducted on a cost-plus or percentage of project cost basis. Such bases are meeting with increased resistance from customers, who prefer fixed prices.

If a fixed price is desired, the scope is best expressed in terms of deliverables, i.e., specifications, reports, drawings, and so on. A fixed price can be obtained if the project is well enough defined before the engineering or architectural contract is let. If one uses this approach, an innovative and high-quality design should not be expected since the design cost is an important consideration. A fixed-price design contract should contain a clause permitting the client to direct changes. Such changes will be at additional cost.

8
Content

General

Considering the vast variety of goods and services that can be specified and the variety of formats that are used for procurement documents, it is obvious that there is no single prescription for content of a specification. Some general precepts can be given, which can be adapted to situations as they arise. Such precepts must be followed with care and judgment.

Table 8-1 shows possible sections of a specification with a list of subjects that might be covered in each. This table is intended to be as inclusive as practical, given the general nature of the subject, so that a writer can use it to check and see that everything needed has been included. Most specifications will need only a portion of the information presented and a format modified accordingly. Some of the items listed might be found in the commercial section of the procurement document, rather than in the specification. They are included here because if the engineer does not prepare these sections, he or she will need information from them when writing the specification. Also, the engineer has an interest in these sections and will want to ensure that they are somewhere in the procurement document.

There are four fundamental principles to be followed in deciding whether to include a subject in a specification. One is that if something is not specified, it will most likely not be furnished.

Occasionally, an unspecified item is provided because it is a manufacturer's standard, but for the most part this principle holds.

A corollary to this principle is that all requirements practical should be in the original specification, prior to granting the order. Once the order is in, the vendor may become less obliging. Competitive pressures

Table 8-1. Potential Specification Contents

Section	Possible subjects within section
1. Introduction	Name of purchaser Name of project Short description of project General statement of scope
2. Scope	List of equipment List of services Battery limits Documentation (general statement) Furnish, erect, test Spare parts (general statement)
3. Work by others	Interfaces with vendor Role of engineer
4. Environmental and site factors	Outdoors Indoors during construction Indoors during operation In warehouse Site geography Lay down space Temporary office space
5. Codes and standards	
6. Technical requirements	Design Construction features Performance State of the art New or used Code compliance Construction procedures Reliability Cleanliness I&C technology Space availability Identification
7. Other project information	Owner-furnished equipment Coordination
8. Materials	Construction materials Paint and coatings Fluids (lubricants, etc.)
9. Tests and inspections	Required tests and inspections Scheduling Witnessing Documentation Purchaser inspections
10. Spare parts	Construction spares Maintenance spares
11. Services by vendor	Erection supervision Start-up and test supervision Technical support Training Obtaining permits

Table 8-1. Potential Specification Contents (*Continued*)

Section	Possible subjects within section
12. Services by purchaser	Electricity Water Others
13. Documentation	Drawings Design instructions Operating manuals Maintenance manuals Code certificates Quality-control records Engineer's certificates Progress reports
14. Environmental restrictions	Discharge air and flue gas Discharge water
15. Quality assurance	
16. Instrumentation and control	Degree of automation Integration with plant control system
17. Project procedures	Correspondence Document approval Change to contract
18. Schedule	
19. Shipment and packaging	Location for passage of title Packing requirements
20. Warranties, bonuses, and penalties	Schedule Performance
21. Instructions to bidders	Time and place of response Information to be submitted Questions, answers, and addenda Scheduled award date Bidders' meeting Site visit
22. Evaluation criteria	Price Payment schedule Discount for future payments Escalation Schedule Qualifications Efficiency Reliability Local manufacture
23. Attachments	Drawings Data sheets Standard specifications
24. Other information	Information in engineer's office Models Site visits Bidders' meeting

Table 8-2. Principles for Specification Contents

1. If something is not specified, it will not be provided.
2. Every requirement increases price.
3. The shorter the specification, the less time it takes to prepare it.
4. The specification is equally binding on both purchaser and vendor.

are much reduced, so the vendor may tend to charge a lot for new requirements in order to make a good profit on them.

The second principle is that every specification requirement tends to increase price. Even a requirement to omit an item may increase price if it causes the vendor to depart from standard practices. Requirements are imposed to ensure performance, to provide adequate quality, or to fulfill legal requirements. If a requirement is not necessary, it should be omitted.

The third principle is that preparation of a specification is itself an economic process. The shorter a specification is, the less time and cost go into preparing it.

Fourth, anything in the specification can be held against the purchaser. If any changes are made in a specification after a proposal is accepted, the vendor may charge extra. Also, a specification contains not only requirements but promises. For example, specified quality of water input to a water treatment plant is a promise. If the water is of lower quality, the water treatment vendor might be excused from performance. Therefore, one must ensure that information put into a specification is correct.

The first principle lengthens a specification, while the second and third tend to shorten it. The correct length for a specification is a matter of judgment and balance, based on individual circumstances. The four principles are stated in Table 8-2.

The remainder of this chapter presents guidance on subjects that might be included in a specification. It is intended to be read in conjunction with Table 8-1. In the remainder of this chapter, section headings are numbered in one-to-one correspondence to Table 8-1.

1. Introduction

Identifying the project a specification is part of is intended to raise the bidders' interest in responding. A bidder's decision to respond to a specification is a free, commercial decision. Bidders are more likely to give an adequate response and a good price if they know the specification-issuing organization and if they identify the project as having substance. If they suspect that the project is merely a study, they will not put much effort into a response. The general statement of scope orients the reader.

2. Scope

The possible contents of this section have been discussed extensively in Chap. 7. A separate section with this title is provided for clarity. A bidder should not have to review the entire specification to determine the scope. If the bidder does have to and misses an item of scope, it will at a minimum increase confusion.

It might result in schedule delays and money problems. In lawsuits, the courts have been known to rule against the purchaser if an item of scope is hidden in other parts of the specification.

3. Work by Others

This section was also discussed in Chap. 7.

4. Environmental and Site Factors

The environmental section can be very involved in some specifications. Environmental factors are crucial to construction contracts, since much of the work is either outdoors or in partially completed buildings. Severe weather has a large effect on schedule and cost. Contractors also need to know about site geography. They need to know how much room is available for storage of equipment and temporary buildings and trailers to house personnel and facilities, and for warehousing. They need to know about road and railroad access and arrangement on site. They need to know about the topography of the site. The civil contractor will need to know about subsoil conditions.

Equipment manufacturers will need to know about the operating environment. Depending on the placement of equipment, this environment can be outdoors and controlled by climate, or indoors and controlled by the building heating, ventilating, and air-conditioning

(HVAC) system. Some equipment, such as large steam generators, is influenced by climate even if located indoors.

Equipment manufacturers also need to know about the environmental conditions where their equipment is stored prior to operation.

Electrical and electronic equipment is especially sensitive to humidity during storage.

Some equipment, such as gas turbines and steam generators, is influenced by legal restrictions on its exhaust gases.

Some of the environmental specifications constitute promises to the vendor. It will not necessarily do to be silent on these points to avoid promises, since, in the absence of information, the vendor can assume normal industry practice. Most electrical equipment, for example, is designed for a maximum temperature of 40°C. If a higher operating temperature is to be used, this fact should be stated.

5. Codes and Standards

This section consists of a list of codes and standards the specified equipment is expected to obey. The bulk of the list is usually made up of codes and standards which are customary in the industry and observed by most manufacturers. The purpose of listing these codes and standards is more to orient the vendor with respect to the quality level expected than anything else. The list will tell the vendor, for example, whether the object of the specification is consumer- or industrial-grade equipment, and whether it is fossil or nuclear power industry. These codes and standards are taken from lists, either explicitly maintained by the engineering department or contained in standard specifications for equipment similar to that being specified.

The rest of the list is made up of codes and standards particularly required by the equipment being specified. These codes and standards may be a subset of the codes and standards referenced above. For example, all electric motors on a project may have to meet National Electrical Manufacturers' Association (NEMA) standards, but only certain ones must meet NEMA standards for explosion-proof motors. In addition to being listed in this section, such codes and standards will be referenced in the section on technical requirements. Standard specifications, such as federal and military specifications, if desired, can be listed here. Either the edition of the code and standard desired should be specified, or a general statement about the edition in effect on the date of the specification should be made.

6. Technical Requirements

This section is the core of the specification. The text of this section is completely dependent on the equipment or service being procured and is fundamentally different for each type of equipment or service.

Design and construction feature specifications are crucial to obtaining suitable equipment. This is the part of the specification where good judgment is of paramount importance. Overspecification drives up costs. Underspecification may result in unsatisfactory equipment. Only a correct balance will result in a good specification.

Often, knowledge of prospective vendors is helpful in determining the balance. Because of their design and manufacturing practices, vendors have limited flexibility in responding to design and construction requirements, except at increased cost. As a result, some vendors produce good-quality equipment whether specified or not. Others, with different practices, produce inferior equipment unless otherwise specified. A simple specification can be used for the former vendors, while a more complex one is required for the latter.

The features required should be specific and verifiable. One can be certain of getting what has been specified only if an inspector can see the feature or verify it by test, or if an engineer can see it on a drawing or document.

Sometimes it is important to specify features with respect to "the state of the art." It might be necessary to have equipment of the latest technology because of weight or space limitations or superior performance. At other times, the extra safety of specifying tried equipment is necessary for increased reliability. Whatever is desired should be clearly specified. It is usually desirable to have information on this point submitted in the proposal so that the development status of the equipment can be verified.

One detail not to be forgotten is whether used equipment is acceptable. It will seldom fit all the application requirements, but if it does, it can be very economical. Used equipment might be acceptable for limited lifetime applications if it is in good condition. In unusual circumstances, it can be used for longer life, if it is in good condition.

If a code is important, or unusual in its application, it should be called out in this section. Vendors have been known to miss codes in the section on codes and standards, assuming that their normal practice will suffice.

There is sometimes a need to specify space availability. Electronic equipment may have to fit in standard racks. HVAC equipment can be very large and needs to fit in specified areas.

Reliability can be a difficult subject to specify. It cannot usually be verified by performance, since the warranty period will be long over before reliability is established. Reliability can be increased by specifying conservative features or by using equipment with a reputation for reliability. To some extent, reliability can be established by requiring submittal of information with the proposal. Such information must be reviewed thoroughly, since there are many ways to bias the presentation of such information. Also, the best vendors may not have the best information. Usually, the approach of specifying conservative design features and dealing with vendors of good reputation is safer.

Cleanliness is a factor in many industries, including food, pharmaceutical, medical, chemical, and power. By cleanliness we mean not the external appearance of the equipment but its internals, the parts that come into contact with the process. Cleanliness means different things in different industries. In the medical industry it means sterility — freedom from bacteria and viruses. In the power industry it means freedom from harmful residues such as chlorides, sulfur, and lead, all of which affect corrosion. Standards for cleanliness should be covered in the technical requirements.

Instrumentation and control (I&C) technology needs to be coordinated throughout any individual project. Most equipment and systems include some instrumentation which feeds signals into the plant I&C system. Such instrumentation must meet the project standard. In the other direction, signals from the plant I&C system must be able to operate the component or system. Controls internal to the component or system, such as overspeed trip on a turbine, need not be coordinated.

Most specifications for systems need a statement as to the degree of automation required. Sometimes local manual operation is satisfactory. Remote operation is more expensive and often required.

This section can include provisions for vendor qualifications. Such provisions are especially necessary for public sector specifications, where restricting bidders is not permitted. Qualifications can be financial or technical. If financial, such provisions will most likely be in the commercial section.

7. Other Project Information

Particularly in construction contracts, a large section on project information is required. This can be construed as a part of the scope, since the function of this information is to define the scope of the project to the contractor.

A large part of this section will be drawings or, properly, reference to drawings, since the drawings themselves are considered attachments to the specification. The drawings will show the contractor what is supposed to be constructed.

The contractor will also need information on "owner-furnished equipment." This term means equipment procured by the owner and turned over to the contractor for erection. In the contractor specification, this information may be general, since the equipment purchase has not been concluded. Exact information will follow as the project progresses.

If there is more than one contractor on the project, the construction management provisions need to be described. Each contractor will depend on the construction manager for coordination. The contractor will need to know what directions will have to be followed and how problems caused by other contractors can be resolved.

8. Materials

Construction materials can be specified in two ways: either by dictating them directly, or by describing the application and letting the vendor select them. Either method can work under appropriate circumstances. If the specification writer selects the materials, he or she accepts responsibility for their success.

Paint and coatings deserve special attention. Often, the equipment vendor supplies a prime coat, with final painting being performed in the field by the erector. In this case, it may be convenient to specify the prime coat by manufacturer and type so that a uniform, compatible top coat can be applied in the field.

Fluids such as lubricating oil and greases are sometimes specified to control quality or provide uniformity. At a minimum, the maintenance force needs to know what was furnished.

9. Tests and Inspections

One sharp vendor I dealt with was willing to certify that his equipment met the specifications but was not willing to provide test results to confirm his statement. He claimed that the tests were not required by the specification. If tests are needed, they must be specified. If the test results are required, their submittal must also be specified.

It is desirable to witness important tests, since test results can be fudged on the spot. One difficulty in witnessing tests is scheduling. Often, tests are part of the vendor's production process, so a delay in the test delays production of other orders as well. The vendor is therefore loath to delay a test until the inspector arrives, and will often refuse to do so. At the beginning of the procurement, it must be emphasized to the vendor that a specified notice — usually 48 hours — of a test must be given. If the inspector cannot get there in that time, the vendor can proceed with the test.

Often, on-site tests are performed by the purchaser. If so, the erection specifications should state this.

10. Spare Parts

Spare parts will be necessary for the life of the project. It is wise to procure spare parts for foreseeable maintenance with the equipment so that they will be on hand when needed. Also, it is more economical for the manufacturer to produce the spares simultaneously with the original equipment. The maintenance forces usually specify what spare parts are required, based on equipment details. These details are not usually available at the time of order. Therefore, the usual specification requirement is a list of spare parts with current prices.

Maintenance spares will be needed from time to time during the life of the equipment. There is not much the original specification can do to control the cost of these spares.

Construction spares are used to make up for damage or pilferage during construction. If the material is furnished by the owner, the appropriate specification must make provision for them. If the equipment is furnished by the contractor, the contractor must use his or her own judgment, since he or she is responsible for the finished product.

Construction spares are usually complete equipment, like valves or circuit breakers, rather than parts.

11. Services by Vendor

In addition to equipment, a vendor is responsible for some services. If needed, they must be specified. Erection supervision and start-up and test supervision are commonly needed services. Technical support is needed for complex equipment such as computers. Sometimes, manufacturer assistance is needed to get environmental permits.

Many services are priced on a dollar-per-hour basis, rather than given a fixed price.

12. Services by Purchaser

The purchaser might provide services such as on-site inspection. If so, the vendor needs to know this, and a statement should be in the specification.

To use another meaning for the word "service," certain hardware services will be furnished by the owner. For example, electricity will be furnished at only a certain frequency, voltage level, power factor, sine wave quality, and interruptibility. The vendor must conform to these restrictions.

Cooling water, if needed, can be supplied with only a certain quality (additives, salinity, etc.), temperature, pressure, and quantity. Compressed air is available at only a certain pressure, moisture content, and quantity.

13. Documentation

One item that increases engineering cost is the submittal of unnecessary documentation by vendors. It takes the time of administrators who handle the documentation. Engineers tend to review any document that arrives at their desk, whether they need to or not. A second item increasing cost is the submittal of improper documentation: unchecked, not in accordance with specification requirements, or not specifically for the project at hand. Sometimes vendors will try to submit data that is generally applicable to their product, but perhaps differing in some details for the exact project.

This section of the specification must be structured so that only required documentation is submitted, and none other. It is also the duty of the entire engineering organization to see that any unnecessary documentation is returned with no action.

This section should define drawing approval rights and what documentation is required for approval and information.

Vendor drawings are often necessary to develop the engineer's drawings. The latter are essentially instructions to other vendors, such as the piping fabricator, and to contractors, such as the electrical contractor who must connect cables to electrical equipment. Vendor drawings are also used to verify specification compliance.

The engineer may need some design guidance to incorporate especially complex systems or equipment into the plant. Such design guides are sometimes called *balance of plant* (BOP) manuals. If one is necessary, it should be called out in the specification.

Instruction, operating, and maintenance manuals may all be necessary. The specification may not need so much to specify their supply as to specify the standards they must meet.

Material, code, and engineer's certificates are often needed for legal reasons or quality-assurance reasons. Other quality-assurance records may be needed for the same reasons. It is sometimes sufficient to require that vendors retain some of the quality-assurance records in their own files for a specified period of time.

A long or complex project may require progress reports to assure that schedules and technical goals are being met.

14. Environmental Restrictions

There are a host of government regulations that can be classified as environmental restrictions. If the regulations are imposed on the complete project, compliance is the responsibility of the owner and appropriate provisions must be in each specification. Obvious examples of such regulations are those dependent on the Clean Air Act and the Clean Water Act, which respectively limit impurities in air and water emitted from the plant. Water temperature is limited also, because of its effect on biological activity and consequently the ecology.

The Federal Communications Commission has restrictions on electromagnetic radiation because of its effect on radio and television transmission and reception.

15. Quality Assurance

A section on quality assurance may be standardized for a given project. It relates mainly to quality-assurance records, since provision for quality control is covered in the section on technical requirements.

16. Instrumentation and Control

This subject has been discussed in Sec. 6, above, on technical requirements. Sometimes a separate section of the specification is dedicated to this subject. If so, it might be standardized for the project.

17. Project Procedures

This information can be contained in the commercial section, if permitted.

18. Schedule

Every project has a schedule. In most simple equipment specifications, it will be sufficient to ask the vendor for a delivery time. If a bidder's delivery time is too long, that bidder can be eliminated from consideration. If documentation, such as vendor drawings, affects the project schedule, a time requirement for its submission may have to be set also.

A specification to a contractor may have an elaborate schedule section. A detailed schedule commitment may be needed from each contractor, since contractors depend on each other for the performance of their work. Conversely, each contractor needs information on when other contractors will complete work he or she is dependent on.

19. Shipping and Packaging

This item may also be in the commercial section. It was discussed in Chap. 7.

20. Warranties, Bonuses, and Penalties

This section is usually separate because of its financial importance. Performance warranty requirements are commonly in the technical section because engineering input is needed to formulate them. Delivery warranties are usually covered in the commercial section. Commercial personnel have important input to this section, wherever located, since the formulation of warranty clauses must be in accordance with the law, and money is directly involved. Under American law, penalties are illegal without a corresponding bonus for better than specified performance.

21. Instructions to Bidders

Much of the information contained in this category can be in the commercial section and standardized for the project. The technical information to be included in the proposal must be specified by the engineers and will vary for each procurement. In specifying information to be submitted, one must realize that bidders do not want to do a large amount of work prior to receiving an order. Better and more proposals will be received if information requirements are minimized. On the other hand, enough information must be requested to ensure that the bidder understands the specification. The proposal should also contain enough information to provide a basis for settling later disputes.

22. Evaluation Criteria

It is only fair to inform the bidders of the evaluation criteria. In the absence of information, the bidders will assume that compliance with the specification and price are the sole criteria.

If a payment schedule is involved, the evaluation will often apply a discount factor to future payments. The discount represents the amount of money earned by placing money in an interest-bearing account at the beginning of the contract, sufficient to meet the payment when due. The interest rate used should be presented in the evaluation criteria.

Future payments are also subject to escalation because of inflation. Escalation formulas are usually proposed by the bidder and are based on the behavior of a published index such as the *Producer Price Index*. The evaluation must compare the formulas proposed by the bidders in accordance with predictions regarding behavior of the indexes. Rules for doing so should be part of the evaluation criteria.

Efficiency is often evaluated by specifying a cost of energy and an operating load factor. Then the capital cost and energy cost are added to determine the evaluated cost. Future energy costs should be appropriately discounted and escalated. All factors used in the analysis should be part of the evaluation criteria. If this type of evaluation is used, a means of verifying the claimed efficiency, such as a test, should be provided. A bonus-penalty clause on tested efficiency is appropriate.

Reliability can be an evaluation criterion. It is difficult to evaluate numerically, since predicted reliability is uncertain.

Government agencies often specify that equipment be manufactured in their own country, or apply a penalty to the cost of foreign equipment such as a requirement that the foreign producer's price must be a certain percentage less than a domestic price to be considered equivalent.

23. Attachments

Drawings are just as valid a means of engineering communication as words. They are attached to the specification and referenced in it.

Data sheets are often used as attachments to specifications. They are treated like drawings.

Sometimes standard specifications are used as attachments. An example might be an electric motor specification used as an attachment to all specifications involving motor-driven equipment.

24. Other Information

Occasionally, a specification will state that some information is available only in the purchaser's or engineer's office. This procedure is used when there is a large mass of information or it is difficult to transmit. For example, soil borings might be available for a civil contract.

Models may be used as part of a specification to explain difficult three-dimensional geometry. Presumably, one model is built and available in the purchaser's or engineer's office. Such a model can be referenced in the contract.

Specifications for site work often require that the bidders inspect the site. This procedure is used to keep the vendor from submitting claims for extra work which would have been apparent had the site been inspected.

Another device for transmitting information is the bidders' meeting. Such a meeting is held to afford bidders an opportunity to ask questions and receive answers. The time and place of the meeting should be in the specification. Attendance at the meeting may or may not be mandatory. Usually, the questions and answers are distributed to all the bidders. Specification addenda may be issued to clarify points brought up at the meeting. The advantage to the bidder in attending the meeting, even if the bidder has no questions, is that all the information presented at the meeting will be received promptly. Since time to prepare the proposal is limited, this is a valuable consideration.

9

Organization, Format, and Style

General

There is one goal that pervades the organization, format, and style of a specification: clarity. The objective of a specification is to obtain equipment or services in accordance with one's requirements economically and on schedule. It is the means for communicating those requirements to the vendor. If one communicates clearly, the chance of attaining this objective is considerably enhanced.

There is no one form for writing a specification that is universally acceptable. Different scopes and different industries have different problems. A very simple case, like ordering minor hardware or office supplies on a purchase order, requires no organization at all. A single clear phrase, not even a complete sentence, will do. It does have to be in the proper format to fit the form. In contrast, a specification for a complete chemical process plant requires a strong organization to keep both writers and readers from being confused.

In some cases, organization and format are dictated by standards or custom. This is the case in much government work. It is also true to an extent in the building construction industry. More often, the project is free to organize and format specifications to meet its needs.

This chapter will describe techniques for developing and carrying out organization, format, and style of specifications. It will not be prescriptive since that would contradict the statement above that no one prescription can apply to all specifications. Rather, suggestions will be given which readers can adapt to their own purposes.

Organization

Organization refers to the major sections of a specification, analogous to chapters in a book. It concerns their titles, the general description of appropriate contents, and their arrangement. An organization is the skeleton on which the contents of a specification are arranged.

The objective of organizing a specification is to enhance clarity. Many people do not read a specification completely, at least not all at once. They read enough to do their jobs. The person in an organization who receives a specification will read enough to decide who to send it to. A sales manager might read enough to decide whether to respond and which proposal engineer to assign. A design engineer might read enough to perform a preliminary design and develop a cost estimate. And so it goes. All these people must be able to locate the information they need. It can be dangerous to the writer if they do not. The reader may miss an important requirement and plan on producing the wrong equipment. In one particular case, a manufacturer assigned a product to the mass production division, rather than to the custom equipment division. This mistake, caused by missing some requirements in a specification, caused delays and cost the manufacturer a lot of money.

The organization also gives instructions to the writer. It defines the writing scope and gives a partial outline for the writing.

The organization also serves as a means of assigning work. It defines what goes into the commercial section, prepared by the purchasing department, and into the specification, prepared by the engineering department. It will also define any standard sections, such as electric motor requirements. This section would be prepared by the electrical engineers and possibly inserted into a specification written by the mechanical department.

Organizing a specification is different from organizing a novel or a report. A novel is designed to be read from beginning to end. Information is presented in a definite sequence and enjoyed most if read in that sequence. A specification, on the other hand, is a compendium of information. Although the information is related, the order of its presentation is of less importance. Some parts can be read without reference to other parts.

The proper organization of a specification is more like a newspaper article, with the most immediately applicable information presented first, and the background information presented later. The front end of

Table 9-1. Typical Equipment Procurement
Document Organization

A. Commercial section
  1. Legal requirements
  2. Commercial requirements
  3. Instructions to bidders
B. Specification
  1. Scope
  2. Codes and standards
  3. Technical requirements
  4. Tests and inspections
  5. Documentation
  6. Information required with proposal
  7. Attachments

Table 9-2. Typical Contractor Procurement
Document Organization

A. Commercial section
  1. Legal requirements
  2. Commercial requirements
  3. Instructions to bidders
B. Specification
  1. Description of project
  2. Scope
  3. Work by others
  4. Codes and standards
  5. Technical requirements for construction
  6. Technical requirements for equipment
  7. Project procedures
  8. Information required with proposal
  9. Attachments

a newspaper article contains information most people will want to read. The back of the same article contains detailed information less people will want to read. The assumption of the editor is that people will read enough to find out what they need to know and then quit.

The difference between a newspaper organization and a specification organization is that some people start reading the specification someplace in the middle. The organization must help these people find the information they need.

Two examples of specification organization are given in Tables 9-1 and 9-2. Each is suitable for a different purpose but designed to be broadly applicable in its field.

It is inevitable that the scope of a specification be presented early. Any reader wants to know what the specification is about, even if he or she does not care about fine points such as battery limits. For a construction specification, the scope cannot be understood without a project description, so the description section comes first, even before the scope. For clarity's sake, it is desirable to keep technical requirements out of the scope section. However, a little overlap is inevitable. It is difficult to define scope without making statements that can be construed as technical requirements.

If a section on work by others exists, it usually follows the scope section, since its function is to clarify the scope.

The codes and standards section comes next. This section is regarded by some as a prelude to the technical requirements. It gives an indication of what kind of equipment is to be supplied. For example, if American Water Works Association standards are referenced, one type of equipment, usable for potable water systems, is indicated. If American Petroleum Institute standards are referenced, a different class of equipment is indicated, even if the subject is pumps in both cases. Because this section's format is a list, it is easy to scan.

Technical requirements come next and often form the bulk of the specification. Most specifications will have one section on technical requirements. Some specifications will have several. This is especially likely in a construction specification where the contractor is to buy much of the equipment.

In an equipment specification, documentation will follow technical requirements. Documentation is less important than technical requirements. A documentation section is less likely to be required in a construction specification, since the constructor presumably builds in accordance with the engineer's drawings.

If there are several construction contractors on a given project, a section on project procedures may be required to tell each contractor how the project will be coordinated.

The section on information required with the proposal is usually placed in the specification, rather than in the commercial section. The engineers need control of the technical information to be presented, since their evaluation depends on it.

The examples of organization given in Tables 9-1 and 9-2 can be used as general guides. If these examples do not fit the case at hand, general principles must be used to develop a suitable organization.

Readers find their way about a specification by using association, or relationships. They expect to find things closely related to one another in the same part of the specification. They also need to have the title of a specification be descriptive of its contents. It is unfair, confusing, and counterproductive to have a requirement, related to others, but hidden in a remote section of the specification.

Obviously, everything in a specification must be in some section. If a requirement does not seem to fit into one of the sections of the standard project organization, one should ask if it is a necessary requirement. If the answer is yes, then one should ask if it can be associated with one of the existing sections by stretching the concept of association a little. If the answer to that question is no, then a new section can be created to cover the requirement.

There is no maximum or minimum length for a section. Complex sections as long as 40 pages are not unknown. If a section exceeds 20 pages, an analysis should be made to see if the section is truly homogeneous. If it seems reasonable to split it, that action should be taken. In limited cases, subsections can be used to limit the length of a particularly unwieldy section.

In many cases, a contractor will use subcontractors. If there is a good probability that this will happen, the technical requirements for each subcontractor should be in a separate section. The prime contractor will then pass the applicable section to each subcontractor, along with such general provisions as might apply. Since this is a common practice, it will be confusing to place say, a few electrical requirements in the plumbing section. Failure to divide the work correctly will not hurt the specification writer contractually, since the writer is not responsible for subcontracting, but dividing the technical requirements in a rational manner will expedite the project.

In addition to the text sections, a specification will often have attachments or appendixes. All attachments must be referenced in some section of the specification, or they will not have any force.

The most common attachment to a specification is drawings. They can be used to define scope, express technical requirements, and describe the project. As a German proverb puts it, "drawings are the language of engineering." As a purportedly Chinese proverb puts it, "one picture is worth a thousand words." In any language, drawings are a very powerful tool. One should use them in preference to words whenever practical. However, superfluous drawings are just as bad as superfluous words. Also, insofar as practical, information on a drawing should be limited to that needed for the specification. Since one drawing may serve many purposes, this latter ideal may not always be attained.

Data sheets are often used to transmit parameters. An example of a data sheet is shown in Fig. 9-1. One specification can have a standard set

		SPEC. No.,_____
		PAGE. No.,_____
		DATE:_____

PROJECT	LOCATION	

SERVICE	NO. UNITS REQUIRED		
LIQUID PUMPED	TEMPERATURE	F	SP. GR.
PUMP NUMBER	PUMP LOCATION		
PUMP ARRANGEMENT DRAWING No.	WEIGHT PERCENT CHEMICAL CONCENTRATION		

PUMP NAME:		PROPOSED BY:
BIDDER/MANUFACTURER		
PUMP SIZE & MODEL No.		
DESIGN CAPACITY GALLONS/HOUR		
DESIGN TOTAL HEAD FT		
DESIGN SUCTION HEAD FT		
BHP @ DESIGN POINT & @ MAXIMUM		
EFFICIENCY @ DESIGN POINT %		
SHUT-OFF HEAD FT		
MAXIMUM SPEED STROKES/MINUTE		
NPSH @ DESIGN POINT FT	AVAILABLE	REQUIRED
INTEMAL RELIEF VALVE, IF SUPPLIED		
MFR. AND MODEL No.		
RELIEF CAPACITY GALLONS/HOUR		
MATERIALS OF CONSTRUCTION		
SUCT. CONN. SIZE, TYPE & RATING		
DISCH. CONN. SIZE, TYPE & RATING		
OUTLINE DIMENSIONS: L x W x H. INCHES		x x
COUPLING MFR. & TYPE IF REQUIRED		
COUPLING GUARD REQUIRED IF COUPLING IS USED		
MANFACTURER'S DRAWING No.		

MATERIALS:	MATERIAL	ASTM No.	MATERIAL	ASTM No.
BODY (SAME AS REAGENT HEAD)				
REAGENT HEAD				
PLUNGER (NOT WETTED)				
CONTOUR PLATE (NOT WETTED)				
DIAPHRAGM IF USED				
BALL CHECKS				
BALL SEATS				
VALVE HOUSING				

GEAR MOTOR		
H.P. & FRAME No.		/
SYNCH. SPEED RPM		
MANUFACTURER		
VOLTS/Ph/Hz		/ /
ENCLOSURE		
INSUL. CL/TEMP. RISE		
SERVICE FACTOR		

WEIGHT: NET PUMP/MOTOR LBS		
-COMBINED SHIPPING LBS		
-OPERATING LBS		

ADDITIONAL REQUIREMENTS:		

Figure 9-1. Positive displacement pump and motor data

of technical requirements and reference data sheets for each item in the scope. Data sheets are preferable to text words. They are not necessarily developed within the specifying organization. Both the Heat Exchange Institute and the Instrument Society of America publish standard data sheets.

Tables are also used to transmit information. An example is shown in Fig. 9-2.

Table No. (cont'd)
Required Equipment and Services

D: District
C: Contractor

B. NSSS related balance of plant systems

Item	Description		Design criteria	Preliminary design	Detail design	Design review
	BWR	PWR				
10.	Main control panels and consoles for NSSS, turbine and generator	Main control panels and consoles for NSSS, turbine and generator	C	D	C	D
11.	Piping for NSSS (Notes 1 and 2)	Piping for NSSS (Notes 1 and 2)	C	D	C	D
12.	Valves for NSSS (Notes 1 and 2)	Valves for NSSS (Notes 1 and 2)	C	D	C	D
13.	Equipment and piping insulation for NSSS (Notes 1 and 2)	Equipment and piping insulation for NSSS (Notes 1 and 2)	C	D	C	D
14.	Wire, cable, and conduit for NSSS (Note 1)	Wire, cable, and conduit for NSSS (Note 1)	C	D	C	D

Note 1: Included are piping (including hangers); valves, except control and special valves; insulation; wire; cable; and conduit

Note 2: Contractor shall furnish specifications covering material requirements, standards, size, and other characteristics. District will provide remaining services under this heading.

Figure 9-2. Equipment table

Fill-in sheets are often used to request proposal information. An example is shown in Fig. 9-3. Bidders are expected to return the fill-in sheets, filled in with data for their products, as part of their proposals. These sheets have the advantage of forcing the bidders to provide directly comparable information. After the proposals are received, fill-in sheets can be pasted together to permit direct comparisons. The assembled fill-in sheets can be used as part of the evaluation report.

<u>Proposal Data</u>

Name of Bidder

3. Chemical Control

   c. (cont'd)

      Volume of standby solution,
      Gallons, minimum

      Poison material content,
               % by wt., minimum

               ppm, minimum

      Temp. of solution, °F minimum

      Pressure maintained in system
               - max. PSIG

               - min. PSIG

      Minimum design flow rates:
      Reactor system: - Hot, full press.

               - Cold, subcritical

               - Refueling

      Driving medium available to
      actuate and maintain flow:

        Mechanical: Pumps

        Pressurized loading: Heaters and gas

        Gravity

      Tabulate the fuel reactivity
      allowances which determine the
      total control requirement.

      Reactivity allowances: $\Delta K/K$
        Cold to hot

        Doppler

        Voids

        Xe

        Sm

        Power shaping

        Burnup

      Total control
      Requirement, maximum

(Trim line)

Figure 9-3. Proposal data

A final part of a specification organization is addenda. Addenda are used in very complex specifications when bidders request clarifications after the bid is issued and prior to bidding. Addenda should reference a section and paragraph in the original specification. Addenda can also be used to record postbid agreements with vendors if the specification is part of the contract.

Once the organization of a specification is established, it is important to follow it. Since the organization is a guide to the reader in finding information, any departure from the organization is misleading. Also, if the organization is not followed, the chance of contradictory information finding its way into the specification is increased. Since related information is to be grouped in a proper organization, contradictions should be near one another and easy to find.

Format

General

Format refers to the organization of material within sections and to the physical arrangement of material on the page. In its greatest detail, it refers to the size of type, the character font, size of margins, and so on.

There is one statement about format that is paramount and fixed without exception. It is this: Every paragraph must be labeled with a number that is related to the organization. In telephone conversation and correspondence, there must be a convenient way to reference statements in the specification. Line numbers will not do, since they can change for the same paragraph if the specification is revised. There are many acceptable numbering systems. The system matters little as long as it is not ambiguous and it can be readily used to locate text.

The goal of format is to produce a specification that is legible, easy to locate requirements in, and uniform in appearance for all specifications on a given project.

Numbering Systems and Paragraphs

A popular way of organizing a specification is by section and paragraph. In this scheme, sections receive a sequential number and paragraphs are designated by decimal point divisions of the section number, e.g.,

3. Technical requirements
   3.1
   3.2
   3.3

This form of organization is usually sufficient, since each requirement can be identified by a number. Sometimes, for clarity, another layer in the hierarchy is provided, e.g.,

   4.0. Thermal duct insulation
     4.1. Concealed conditioned air ductwork
     4.1.1
     4.1.2
     4.2. Exposed conditioned air ductwork
     4.2.1
     4.2.2

The second form is also acceptable and may provide superior clarity and convenience. The important point is that each paragraph has a number.

One may not be free to choose a paragraph numbering system. In the building industry, for example, it is wise to use the 16-division format developed by the Construction Specifications Institute. It is a de facto standard for the industry. Government and military usage often also forces one to use a predetermined numbering system.

If a specification has been issued and a new paragraph is needed, the paragraph should be added at the end of a sequence and the next number assigned to it. In the first example above, the new paragraph might be 3.4. If a new number is needed in the middle of a sequence, it can be designated by a letter, e.g., 3.2B. The original paragraph 3.2 becomes 3.2A. This procedure preserves the original number for all subsequent paragraphs. If a paragraph is deleted, it should appear in the specification as, for example, 3.2 (deleted).

Often, a paragraph will contain lists. Each item in a list should be provided with a designator, either a number or a letter.

Paragraph Structure

The dictionary defines "paragraph" as a subdivision of a chapter. For a specification, that definition can be supplemented by saying that a paragraph is a group of sentences having a common topic.

Paragraphs contribute to the goal of clarity by collecting all the requirements on one topic in one place. Use of paragraphs also helps the writer to express ideas logically.

Since a paragraph in a specification expresses requirements on a single topic, they are usually short. If a paragraph exceeds four sentences, it should be examined with the idea that it might be better to break it into two. Contrary to English composition practice, one-sentence paragraphs are completely acceptable.

Detailed Format

Detailed format is another tool used in the effort to make a specification clear and definite. Every organization should have a format guide. It will be of interest mostly to the word processing group, who physically form the documents. The engineers need not know the guide in detail, but they should be generally aware of the format standard so as to minimize difficulties in translating their drafts. The individual engineers do not dictate format. They must use the company standard.

A proper format will aid the reader in finding information. The title and number of each section should be prominent, preferably centered on the page or underlined, and with a blank line above and below it. Paragraphs should also be separated by blank lines. Indentations should be limited, since they waste space. Lists should be indented.

All specifications should be printed on 8½ by 11-inch paper, or its metric equivalent. Use of any other page size will cause difficulties in word processing, printing, and filing.

Most other questions of format need not concern the engineer. Many of them can be settled by using the default settings in the word processing program. One word processing program should be used throughout the organization so that any operator can process any document. Some engineers will want to operate the word processing equipment themselves, since they can compose as they type. Print for specifications as issued should be letter-quality or near letter-quality. Draft quality can be used for internal drafts.

Style

General

A dictionary might define "style" as "manner or mode of expression in language; way of putting thoughts into words." Specifications make definite demands on style which are different from the demands made by other writing applications. Specification writing serves the goals of clarity and precision. The vendor must understand what is required by the specification and that everything must be complied with. There is no room for ambiguity in a specification.

To attain the goals of clarity and precision, one may have to sacrifice aesthetics. If a specification writer was trained in English composition at a good school, he or she will have to modify his or her ideas of style.

Sentence Structure

There are two acceptable sentence structures for a specification. The most common structure is the simple declarative sentence. This is a sentence that makes a declaration, with a subject, verb and a direct object. For example,

The rotor shall be 10 percent chrome steel.

The pump assembly consists of a pump, motor, and base plate.

Such declarative sentences state clear and definite requirements.

A few people prefer the mandative sentence, that is, one of the form

Make the rotor of 10 percent chrome steel.

Include a pump, motor, and base plate in the pump assembly.

Both modes of expression are acceptable. I prefer the declarative sentence, since it can be used to specify the result, rather than the action to be taken. When the inspector works, it is the result, rather than the action taken, that is visible.

If a sentence has a complex structure, it is most likely not clear. It should be divided into two or more simple declarative sentences. Sentences can often be clarified by using lists, for example,

The pump assembly consists of the following:
   a. Pump
   b. Driving motor
   c. Shaft coupling
   d. Base plate
   e. Pump-mounted instrumentation

Requirements are not necessarily expressed in complete sentences. For example, a section of a specification could be written as follows:

1. Scope
   a. Ductwork
   b. Ductwork expansion joint
   c. Exhaust gas damper
   d. Controls and instrumentation

The list expresses the equipment scope adequately, if informally.

Vocabulary

In selecting words to be used in a specification, one must remember that clarity and precision are the key. One should particularly avoid the temptation to show off a wide vocabulary. If the reader does not understand a word, the writer has failed to communicate.

One should also be sure to use a word in the sense accepted by the industry, because that is the way it will be understood. If in doubt about the accepted meaning of a word, one should look through technical journals to find examples of its use. Precision in the use of technical words is necessary. A diaphragm valve, for example, is different from a diaphragm-operated valve.

Once one word is used in a specification, its use should be continued for that concept. Do not say "furnish" in one place and then use "supply" in another to mean the same thing. Do not refer to the vendor in one place and to the supplier in another. Your intent will be misunderstood. The reader will often assume there is some subtle difference involved that forced the writer to use two different words. This rule is contrary to that often used in English composition, where repetition of the same word is considered inelegant.

One should avoid legalistic language. A specification is written by engineers and used by engineers. Both writer and reader are oriented toward achieving results, and the language should be suitable for that purpose. The language should be simple and direct.

There should be no superfluous words in a specification. They only obscure communication and cause trouble. If even one word is unnecessary, it should be eliminated.

In a specification, "shall" is preferred over "will." Both words indicate future tense, but "shall" indicates a requirement, while "will" is merely a prediction.

A phrase to be avoided is "et cetera." Vendors tend to ignore it, since it has no specific meaning. A somewhat more acceptable, but still weak, phrase is "for example." Any statement in a specification should be clear enough that examples are not required.

Another word to be avoided is "intent." Some engineers are fond of specifying that the intent of a code should be met. What they have in mind is a vague concept that the essence of a code should be met, but not any troublesome little provisions that do not fit the case at hand. Nobody knows what the intent of a code is, as distinct from its expressed text. To avoid fruitless debate with the vendor, the code to be used should be specified, and any exceptions to that code should also be specified.

The phrase "and/or" should be avoided. Its meaning is not clear. Another weak word is "prefer." An example of its use would be a statement like, "Both stellite and colmonoy valve trim are acceptable, but stellite is preferred." Many vendors will not pay any attention to it, unless they are told that the evaluation will be based on meeting the preference. Then a preference may as well be a requirement.

Techniques

There are many little language techniques helpful in writing specifications. The use of the term "or equal" leads to many controversies. It is used by specifying a manufacturer and perhaps a model and then adding "or equal" or "or approved equal." You can be sure that any equal suggested by a contractor is cheaper than what was specified. Prior to bid, if approval for a substitute is requested, and the specifier considers the substitute equal, approval can be granted. To be fair, other bidders should be allowed to make the same substitution. If approval for a substitute is requested after acceptance of a proposal, the buyer should request a price reduction.

There is a principle in law that "whatever is not included is excluded." This makes blanket statements preferable to lists that may later prove to be incomplete. It is better to say "The vessel shall be in accordance with the ASME Code, Section 8," than to say "The vessel shall be designed and fabricated in accordance with the ASME Code, Section 8." In the latter case, the vessel might not be inspected or certified in accordance with the code.

It is desirable to avoid repeating the same data in different parts of the specification. It is most embarrassing to have others find that data was changed in an update in one section of the specification, but not in another.

Another legal point to be remembered in writing a specification is that words are construed against the party that wrote them. In other words, if there is doubt about what the specification means, a court would interpret the specification in favor of the vendor. Although our aim is to fulfill the specification without going to court, this principle will strengthen the vendor in negotiations. It is another reason to write a clear specification.

One should strive for a degree of consistency from one specification to the next. It will simplify specification preparation. Also, if an organization sends specifications to the same bidder repeatedly, it will acquire a reputation. If the specifications are reasonably consistent, they will be understood with ease, and better service and prices will result.

10
Administrative and Legal Matters

General

Although engineers, by definition, are concerned with technical matters, they must have enough knowledge of business, commercial, and legal matters to fulfill their objectives. The objective of a specification has been defined as the on-schedule, economical procurement of adequate equipment or services. This objective cannot be attained without some appreciation of legal and commercial principles.

A specification usually forms part of a contract. In case of a major dispute, it will be construed according to legal principles and ultimately may be interpreted by administrators, lawyers, arbitrators, and judges. Unless one is acquainted with the principles these people use, it may be difficult to enforce a specification.

One would hope that the specification would be fulfilled without resorting to these extraneous people. However, many recipients of specifications have a degree of training in legal and commercial matters. Even if no major procurement difficulties ensue, it will help in communicating with such people and in settling minor disputes if the specification engineer has corresponding knowledge.

In addition, the people who prepare the commercial and legal parts of the procurement document often do not have an appreciation of the equipment or services being procured. Although the engineers cannot control the contents of the commercial section, they should at least appreciate what is there, how it affects their work, and how to formulate their work to complement it. If engineers are knowledgeable and tactful, they can influence the contents of the commercial section to meet their goals. Engineers who are neither will be told to mind their own business.

The author recommends that every specification engineer read a book on commercial law. Two examples are given (see Refs. 1 and 2). Even if lawyers are not involved, writing a specification on a correct legal basis will aid enforcement.

Coordination with the Commercial Section

There is no hard-and-fast rule on what is to be included in the commercial section and what in the specification. The line between the two depends on the organization and the project. The client often has a voice in the matter also.

The commercial section is usually standard for at least a project, while the specification is different for each procurement action. Therefore, commercial matters peculiar to an individual procurement may be included in the specification for convenience in production. If the subject is purely commercial, the text will probably be provided by the purchasing department and assigned its own section.

The procurement document will also contain technical information that is standard for the project. In a borderline case, such information will be construed as commercial, so it can be included in the commercial section for convenience of production. If it cannot be so construed, it will be placed in a section of its own or in an appendix.

Occasionally, the same subject is covered in both the commercial section and the specification. This is the engineer's only choice if the subject is not suitably covered in the commercial section. The author once had to resort to this practice for drawing submittals. The commercial section then had a section on drawing submittals, and the specification had a section entitled Technical Drawing Submittals. This is not a good practice, since it can lead to confusion and contradictions, but it may be the only solution if the commercial people are inflexible regarding the text of their section.

In any event, engineers should be aware of what is in the commercial section and coordinate their work with it so that all necessary items are covered and no contradictions occur.

Price Requirements

Price requirements are a commercial matter, but the engineers are deeply involved in their formulation. The following bases are often used.

Fixed price. This means a fixed-dollar amount for a fixed scope and requirements. It is the most risk-free basis from the fiscal point of view, since the cost is known. It is the easiest to administrate, since it simply requires payment on a signal or signals contained in the contract, such as notice of delivery. It also requires the most thorough specification, since all requirements are set forth in the contract.

Cost-plus percentage fee. This means that the buyer covers all the vendor's costs, plus a proportionate amount, as the project proceeds. The buyer can then change requirements during the course of the project. The initial specification need not be thorough. This is fiscally the most risky method, since the vendor has little incentive to reduce costs. It is also the most difficult to administer, since a prudent purchaser will audit the vendor's books to see that costs are properly allocated. It is used where the specification is vague to the point that a price cannot be determined. This approach reduces technical risk since the work can be changed as the product progresses. Schedule risk is high since the vendor has no incentive to finish.

Cost-plus fixed fee. This is a variation on cost-plus percentage fee. It affords the vendor a mild incentive to reduce cost, since the percentage fee is inversely proportional to the cost.

Time and materials. In this arrangement, time of labor is paid for at a fixed rate for each category (e.g., senior engineer) of labor. Cost of materials is passed on to the client, perhaps with a percentage markup. This procedure eases administration compared to a cost-plus arrangement, since only time records and material invoices need be audited. It affords the vendor no incentive to finish the work. Specification requirements are similar to those for cost-plus contracts.

There are many variations on these basic arrangements, such as cost plus with a ceiling, or complete cost plus up to a point, with only partial coverage thereafter.

The simplest price arrangement for a fixed-price contract is payment upon delivery. It is also the most favorable to the buyer, since payment is deferred until the latest time practical. Vendors will agree to this arrangement only if they trust the buyer to pay. Vendors who do not trust the buyer may insist on earlier payment, perhaps at the time the order is placed. Then the buyer must decide if the vendor can be trusted.

For a large contract and a long delivery time, the vendor will usually insist on progress payments, that is, a series of periodic payments made from time of order to time of delivery. Usually, one final payment is made after delivery. The rationale for such payments is that the vendor's capital would otherwise be occupied in expenditures for the project. The vendor would rather use the buyer's capital to finance the project.

Long delivery times also lead to uncertainties due to inflation or the cost of raw materials. If payment occurs more than 1 year after order, most vendors will insist on an adjustment usually called *escalation*. Such adjustments are commonly based on indexes published by the federal government or on publicly recorded prices. A well-known example of the former is the *Consumer Price Index*. Examples of the latter are the prices of commodities as traded on commodities exchanges. An individual index or a combination of indexes may be used in an effort to indicate accurately the effect of inflation and future raw material cost on a vendor's cost.

Long delivery times also lead to uncertainties in the relationships of national currencies. If a price is quoted, for example, in German marks, and the dollar weakens against the mark after the price is agreed upon, the price in dollars would be appreciably higher at the time of delivery. This factor will become more important as commerce becomes more international. It can be eliminated as a risk by requiring price quotations in the buyer's currency. One might also not get the best price that way.

The use of indexes and the influence of foreign currencies must be factored into the economic evaluation of proposals, which is usually the engineer's duty. Even if the prices from two vendors are the same in today's dollars, the escalation provisions, time of payment, and fluctuation in currency exchange rates may show an appreciable difference in the evaluated prices. This subject will be discussed in more detail in the next chapter.

A last detail in pricing is the period of validity. A procurement document should specify that prices in a proposal must be guaranteed for a period of time called the *period of validity*. This period should last until the proposals can be evaluated and an order placed. The engineer has an interest in seeing that the period of validity is long enough for the work to be done.

Repetitive Procurement

So far, most of the discussion has been based on a single procurement action. It is not uncommon that the same item is procured repetitively, using the same basic specification. Contract procedures can vary with successive procurements. If the item in question must be developed, the first procurement may be on a cost-plus basis. Once the item is developed, subsequent procurements might be on a fixed-price basis. Open bidding might not be feasible, since the original manufacturer has the advantage of knowledge, unless the contract arrangements included provision for technology transfer. In this case, the subsequent procurements may be based on a negotiation. The buyer should expect that the manufacturer will give price reductions, based on a "learning curve." The manufacturer's costs should decrease as experience is gained, and the manufacturer should be willing to pass on at least a portion of the savings to the client.

Evaluation Criteria

Often, price is not the only criterion in selecting a vendor. In many industries such as aircraft and marine, weight and space can be criteria. In service contracts, the quality of people offered may be more important than price. Evaluation criteria are often placed in the commercial section, since they are closely related to price and since the purchasing department or corporate management often makes the final choice of vendor.

Price is usually the basic evaluation criterion, and other criteria are related to it. For example,

An additional kilowatt of output is worth $400.

A reduction of one BTU per kilowatt hour is worth $40.

Each pound in weight will be penalized $50.

Each kilowatt of electricity required will be penalized $600.

Such explicit criteria are easy to evaluate, and they provide bidders with a firm basis for optimizing their product. The values fixed for such criteria must be realistic or the bidders will be led to ridiculous designs.

Table 10-1. Evaluation Criteria for Service Contract

Item	Weight (%)
Wage rate for each chargeable employee classification	20
Overhead rate	20
Previous company experience	15
Qualifications of proposed project manager	15
Qualifications of proposed project team	10
Location of work performance	10
Quality of project control system	10

There must also be reliable proof in the proposals that the criteria will be met when the project is complete.

Once an evaluation criterion is specified, it is only fair to use it in the evaluation. If the proper thought was given to developing the criterion, a good result will be obtained.

Another type of evaluation criterion is the qualitative one, usually used with a point system. Such criteria are often used in service contracts and might be expressed as in Table 10-1.

Another evaluation criterion that has been mentioned previously is the state of the art. This indicates a judgment that the equipment proposed is either the latest development, promising better performance, or an established technology, promising an established record of reliability and maintainability. If a judgment is to be made on this score, it should be stated in the specification.

Vague evaluation criteria may scare off qualified bidders. If they do not understand a criterion, they may conclude that it was stated so that the contract could be awarded to a favored bidder. Vague criteria are also hard to apply in the evaluation.

Warranties

Warranty and guarantee are two closely similar terms. Warranty is the preferred term in specifications.

A *performance warranty* is a quantitative statement made by the supplier about performance, accompanied by a promise to pay a specified sum if the statement is not so. An example is a statement that a steam generator will produce a specified number of pounds per hour of steam at a specified temperature and pressure when supplied with feedwater at a specified temperature and pressure. If the steam generator does not perform as warrantied, the supplier will pay a specified sum, usually proportional to the deficiency.

Performance warranties deserve careful attention from the specification writer because, generally, a great deal of money is involved. The vendor will pay careful attention to a warranty statement for the same reason, and a negotiation may occur before a statement satisfactory to both parties is attained. Warranty statements must be clear and definite, since the vendor will not pay without clear proof that it is due. At the time of warranty performance, most of the money and equipment has changed hands. The vendor has little incentive to pay except continued good relationships and the threat of a lawsuit the vendor will lose.

The ideal condition for establishing completion of a performance warranty is a test witnessed by both parties and according to a procedure agreed to by both sides. Such a test will provide the clear proof that the warranty statement has or has not been met. The test can be performed either in the manufacturer's shop or in the completed facility. In either case, both sides must have access to the test equipment and the raw test data. It is important to establish as specific and complete a basis for the test as practical in the specification. It is often useful to reference a code such as one of the ASME performance test codes.

Equipment warranties are also useful in specifications. These are familiar because almost all consumer equipment comes with such a warranty, volunteered by the vendor. An *equipment warranty* is usually a simple statement that the equipment will be free of fault for a specified period of time. Time can be calendar time or some related parameter such as, for an automobile, miles operated. The definition of a fault might be difficult in some cases and might be subject to negotiation. The remedy is usually repair or replacement.

All specifications should call for equipment warranties. The length of the warranty should be as long as can be negotiated. The warranty period should start when the equipment is placed in service, not when it is delivered. On construction projects, there can be a long gap between the two events. It is not unknown to have a warranty which starts on delivery expire before the equipment is operated.

The minimum remedy should be repair or replacement of the faulty equipment. Such a remedy does not eliminate the buyer's economic loss. The buyer is still deprived of the equipment while it is being repaired or replaced. As a consequence, the buyer's plant may not be able to operate, or it may be forced to operate at partial capacity. Also, it costs money to remove and reinstall the equipment. A warranty is therefore not a proper substitute for known quality of equipment, only additional assurance.

Unless there is a specific statement to the contrary in the contract, all equipment comes with a "warranty of merchantability." This warranty is a feature of the Uniform Commercial Code, which is law in most states.

Loosely speaking, it is a warranty that the goods are fit for the ordinary purposes for which they are sold. The specifier should be careful that the vendor does not try to remove this warranty by inserting words in the contract.

Schedule Requirements

There are several schedule aspects to be covered in a specification. Schedules were discussed in Chap. 1, where the object was to schedule production of the specification. Here, the object is to describe what the specification should say about the schedule.

All schedules are related to the objective of completing the project on time.

In the specification, the first schedule item to be considered is the date for the receipt of proposals. The time set aside for preparation of proposals should be sufficient to permit a respectable job. Rushed proposals may result in high prices and nonresponsive proposals. The time requirement varies from 2 weeks for a simple specification to several months for a complex project.

Time for proposal evaluation is not stated directly in a specification, since it is not a requirement for the bidders. The specification should state a required period of validity for the proposal, including price and delivery time. The validity period must be long enough that the evaluation can be completed and an order placed within that period.

The specification should either state a required delivery date or ask the bidder to supply one. In either case, the specifying engineer should know what a reasonable delivery time is. If the bidders supply the delivery time, it can be used as an evaluation criterion. If a delivery time is not in agreement with project requirements, the bid can be rejected.

The specification may have a bonus-penalty clause for schedule if it is considered of major importance.

The specification should also have a requirement for delivery of vendor information, based on the engineer's schedule for performing the work. From the engineer's point of view, this schedule can be independent of equipment delivery schedule, although both are dictated by project requirements and are thus, in a subtle way, linked. The project often cannot be completed without engineer's drawings based on vendor information. Unfortunately, vendors often make light of information requirements. The engineer must vigorously follow up on information requirements and, if necessary, withhold permission to fabricate until information is approved.

Schedules for erection contracts are more complex than those for equipment contracts. An erection contract might contain a detailed schedule the contractor is expected to meet, coordinated with other contractors and equipment suppliers on the project. It may also contain a schedule for delivery of the engineer's drawings. These latter schedules constitute promises the purchaser will be responsible for.

Regulations

All projects are required to meet government regulations. One usually thinks of regulations in conjunction with the building industry, with local building codes and their regulations. However, it is hard to think of a project that is completely free of government regulations. Even computers must conform to Federal Communications Commission regulations on electromagnetic radiation, Occupational Safety and Health regulations, and so on.

There are two ways that these regulations can be implemented in specifications. One way is to specify features in the technical section of the specification that carry out the regulation. In this case the purchaser retains complete responsibility for obeying the regulation. The other approach is to reference the regulation in the specification, with a requirement that it be met. This procedure does not relieve the owner of any responsibility, since the government will expect the owner to obey the regulations, but it does shift the work of interpreting the regulation and applying it to the equipment to the vendor, where it belongs. The vendor has probably seen the regulation in past orders and knows how to design equipment to meet it.

Although the vendor may know how to implement regulations in a product, the vendor may not know which regulations apply to a given project. Some regulations vary depending on industry and location. That is why the specification writer must reference them.

It is one of the specification writer's duties to research the applicability of regulations. Some regulations are almost universal. For example, the Occupational Safety and Health Administration's regulations will apply in any industrial situation. Some regulations are obvious. Nuclear Regulatory Commission regulations will apply in any nuclear installation, and the local building regulations will apply to almost any structure. In the absence of personal experience, advice from an experienced associate is the best guide, followed by review of existing specifications. The writer must be careful that he or she understands the choice of regulations in existing specifications. Personnel from regulatory agencies, like the town engineer's office, can also be helpful.

A list of federal regulating agencies is given in Chap. 2.

Voluntary Codes

Many codes and standards are useful in specifications, even if they are not required by law. A partial list of agencies publishing codes and standards is given in Chap. 2. Absent experience on the writer's part, advice from an experienced associate or use of previous specifications are the best guides to what codes and standards should be specified.

Shipping and Packing

Particularly on international projects, packaging and point of delivery are important. The most common practice is to use the FOB concept. As a reminder, this abbreviation means "free on board"; that is, the vendor's responsibility ceases when the object is placed on board the shipper's vehicle at the vendor's factory. From that point on, any damage is the shipper's responsibility. Other delivery points can be specified. A popular one is free alongside ship (FAS). In that case, the vendor's responsibility ceases when the object is at a port, dockside, and alongside the ship, and it is up to the shipper to actually get the object into the ship. This arrangement relieves purchasers of the burden of coping with shippers inside the vendor's country. Another possibility is to hold the vendor responsible for shipment to a port in the purchaser's country. This arrangement relieves purchasers of the burden of coping with anyone outside their own countries. Most vendors will not want to go further, because they are now dealing in another, probably unfamiliar, country.

It is sometimes important to specify packaging requirements. If the point of use is in the commercialized part of the world and on the same continent as the factory, a packaging requirement may be superfluous. However, even such rugged items as stainless-steel pipe may need special consideration even under these circumstances. Sensitive equipment and equipment delivered across an ocean or to tropical or less-developed parts of the world will certainly need special consideration.

Packaging requirements, if they can be standardized for the project, will usually be placed in the commercial part of the procurement document. If special requirements are needed for equipment in one particular specification, these requirements will generally be in the specification.

Patents

If a vendor infringes a patent, the buyer may acquire a burden. For example, use of the equipment might be enjoined. In this case, the vendor is responsible, but the buyer may have a problem.

If a design is described in the specification and infringes a patent, the buyer may be held responsible. Vendors may avoid responsibility by claiming they only did what was required. This is especially possible in a construction contract, since the contractor might neither use nor sell the patented item.

Other Administrative Items

There are many other items in the commercial section which the engineer need not be concerned with. As a general rule, the engineers should not interfere. The commercial people know their craft. Engineers should be aware of what is in the commercial section to protect their own interests and to ensure that the commercial people, in their technical ignorance, do not make a mistake.

References

1. Ronald A. Anderson and Walter A. Kumpf, *Business Law*, 9th ed., Southwestern Publishing Company, Cincinnati, Ohio, 1972.
2. John D. Donnell, A. James Barnes, and Michael B. Metzger, *Law for Business*, Richard D. Irwin, Homewood, Illinois, 1980.

11
Proposal Evaluation Techniques

General

Chapter 4 viewed proposal evaluation as a process, from the point of view of a manager. This chapter will view the same activity from the point of view of the worker who must carry it out. The worker is interested in the techniques that must be applied, starting with the preparation necessary to ensure a successful effort.

Evaluation can be a time- and energy-consuming task. A major evaluation effort can consume 2000 person-days of work. Therefore, it is necessary to be efficient and plan the work to minimize the time. Efficiency, however, cannot be allowed to detract from the goal of procuring satisfactory equipment or services economically.

Bidders List

The evaluation effort starts with establishing the bidders list. Engineers can limit their work in evaluations by seeing that only bidders who are reliable and produce adequate-quality equipment which fits the needs of the prospective procurement are permitted on the list. Since the original bidders list is usually established at the beginning of a project, the engineers who help prepare it must know their equipment well enough to project general equipment requirements and identify likely bidders. They will be continuously pruning their lists by deleting unsatisfactory vendors and also searching for prospective additions to the list. This search is accomplished by talking whenever practical to operating or maintenance personnel and to fellow specifiers. Prospective new suppliers are also located by reading technical literature and listening to salespeople.

Letting a vendor on the bidders list should not be a casual process. The purchasing department will take care of commercial matters. On the technical side, the engineers should assure themselves that additions to the bidders list have a record of adequate quality and that they regularly build equipment in accordance with the contract. Information on these points is best gained from one's own previous experience with the vendor or from the vendor's previous customers. Often, the client will have pertinent experience from previous projects. If one lets a bidder be added to the list without a thorough investigation, it may lead to trouble later when the bidder performs unsatisfactorily.

One way of deciding whether to let a bidder on the bidders list is to ask the question: Would we be willing to give an order to this firm? If the answer is no, there is no point in letting the bidder on the bidders list and spending time to evaluate the bidder's proposals.

If procurement rules do not permit a bidders list, as is often the case for public agencies, a qualification statement can often be placed in the specification. This can be, for example, a simple statement that the bidders must show that they have produced similar goods in the past. Such a statement will eliminate some unqualified bidders, but it will not eliminate the ones who submit a proposal in spite of a lack of qualifications. Such bidders should be eliminated as the first step in the evaluation. Other bidders will exaggerate their qualifications. Eliminating such bidders requires review and investigation. As with any other provision in a specification, a qualifications requirement must be clear and definite to avoid later trouble.

Specification Writing

Specification writing is performed with evaluation in mind. There will be specific passages in the specification regarding evaluation. Also, most provisions in the specification will be used in evaluation.

Before writing a specification, one must have an idea what the evaluation criteria will be. Unless otherwise expressed, they will be price and conformance to the specification. These two criteria can be easy to evaluate, but one must decide what weight to give each of them. If a specification is well written by a knowledgeable engineer and the bidders list is adequate, total conformance to the specification is expected and the evaluation can be based on price alone. If the evaluation will be based on other criteria, they should be specifically stated in the specification so that the vendors can formulate their proposals accordingly. Examples of evaluation criteria were given in Chap. 10.

The specification should include requirements for information to be transmitted in the bidders' proposals as needed for the evaluation. It is not sufficient to assume that the necessary information will be volunteered. The transmittal requirements should be coordinated with the section of the commercial document covering instructions to bidders.

The specification should include fill-in sheets as described in Chap. 9. These sheets force bidders to give explicit information in a form that can be easily evaluated. The fill-in sheets should be formulated so that all important points in the evaluation are covered. It is not necessary to request information on all specification requirements, since that standard requires too much effort on the part of both the writer and the bidder. If bidders are asked to fill in too much information, they tend to become sloppy about it. Contradictions between the fill-in sheets and other sections of the proposal are a possibility for confusion. Therefore, the specification should contain a provision that any contradictions in the proposal will be construed in favor of the buyer.

One should realize that fill-in sheets do not express requirements. On the contrary, they merely request information for use in the evaluation. The requirements are in the text of the specification.

All fill-in sheets should include a requirement that exceptions to the specification be listed. Such an item decreases the chance that an exception will slip by unnoticed.

The use of fill-in sheets does not eliminate the need for a careful review of proposals. Undetected contradictions can exist.

Even if the buyer has a legal right to the favorable resolution of contradictions, the schedule, as a minimum, will suffer while the contradictions are resolved.

The specification should also contain requirements on what information the bidder is to furnish for evaluation besides the fill-in sheets. If this is not done, the evaluation may have to be performed in ignorance of important points. One can assume that the goods will be in accordance with the specification in the absence of contrary information, but such an assumption can lead to surprises later. The bidders may misunderstand the specification.

The specification should discourage the submittal of excess information. All information submitted must be reviewed. Excess information increases evaluation labor and may obscure the really significant information.

Clear, explicit specifications facilitate evaluation by providing clear directions to the evaluator. It is easy to check a proposal for conformance if one needs only to search for responses to explicit requirements. A

Table 11-1. Checklist—Writing for Evaluation

1. Have fill-in sheets been included?
2. Is there a specific requirement that the bidder transmit the fill-in sheet responses in the proposal?
3. If a fill-in sheet is inappropriate, has the bidder been required to transmit information needed for evaluation in another form?
4. Has transmission of economic (price, payment schedule, etc.) information needed for evaluation been required, either in the specification or the commercial section?
5. Is the specification properly coordinated with Instructions to Bidders?

vague specification leads to proposals that are hard to compare because different bidders respond with different solutions to the problems posed by the requirements. One must then decide which solution is preferable and must often put a money value on the preference. This is extra labor and often leads to controversies.

In many public bids, the bidders are not allowed to modify their offers once they are submitted. This practice is considered necessary to avoid secret deals being made. It also shortens the evaluation, since negotiations with the bidders are not required. It also increases the need for a clear, complete specification, since the evaluation must be based solely on the specification and the proposals. No clarifications will be possible.

If bid modifications are not allowed, the apparently successful bidder should be informed of any contradictions discovered in the bidder's proposal and the resolution used by the purchaser. If the bidder does not accept the resolution, the bid can be withdrawn, and the award can be made to the next higher evaluated bidder.

A checklist on writing for evaluation is presented in Table 11-1.

Conducting the Screening Review

The project manager will deliver the proposals to the evaluating engineers. A date will be established for delivery of the evaluation report, if a formal report is required. If it is not, a date will be established for completion of the evaluation and transmittal of its conclusion.

The proposals will first receive a screening review. This is a cursory inspection, used primarily to plan the evaluation. Any patently inappropriate proposals can be dismissed at this stage to save work. The reasons for deeming a proposal inappropriate must be recorded for inclusion in the report.

The fill-in sheets transmitted by the bidders should be pasted together to form a matrix. It can be scanned to give a rapid comparison of the bids. The matrix may be used as an illustration in the evaluation report.

Assuming that the person-days to be used in the evaluation are limited, the screening review will result in a decision about whether the economic evaluation or the technical evaluation will be done first. The criterion for this decision is which sequence is more efficient. If several proposals appear technically satisfactory but the prices vary, the economic evaluation can be done first. Then, only the two or three lowest-priced proposals need receive a technical review.

The screening review will also be used to confirm the person-day budget and the schedule for the evaluation.

The screening review will also result in a plan for conducting the evaluation, including a list of items deserving careful attention.

Conducting the Technical Review

The basic purpose of the technical review is to confirm that the specification has been met. The first step is a thorough review of the fill-in sheets, using specification requirements as a standard. Differences are noted and evaluated. Each difference should be recorded with an evaluation of its significance. If insignificant, the matter is dropped. If significant, an evaluation must be made about whether the difference is a deficiency or exceeds specification requirements. If the former, a decision must be made whether to reject the proposal or to assess a money penalty, assuming that is permitted by the bidding rules. If the difference exceeds specification requirements, the difference must be assessed and a decision made regarding a money credit. Many organizations will not permit such credits, in the interest of reducing cost as much as practical while meeting the standard of quality demanded by the specification. If such credits are permitted, the amount of the credit must be established on the basis of value to the owner. For example, if a bidder provides a superior material, the credit might be based on reduced maintenance cost or increased usage factor. Such estimates are often difficult to make. The evaluator is often tempted to make a simpler estimate, that is, the extra cost the bidder accepts. This type of estimate has no validity. The conclusions of this review are recorded for use in the evaluation report.

After the fill-in sheets have been reviewed, it is time to turn to the text of the proposals. These are reviewed in the same manner as the fill-in sheets. In addition, one must review information in the proposals that does not address specification requirements. It may reveal a deficiency in the goods or an advantage unforeseen by the specification writer. If significant, this information must also be evaluated.

It is often found that proposals need clarification. In commercial work, it is usually permissible to seek such clarifications. However, the evaluators must be careful to follow company procedures and industry practices in seeking clarification. The purchasing department is responsible for relationships with bidders. Some purchasing departments insist that all contacts with bidders be made through them. Others will permit engineers to contact bidders for technical clarifications only. The general rule is that if money is involved, the purchasing department must also be involved. In any case, the purchasing department must be kept informed.

Seeking clarifications takes time. It must be included in the person-day estimate. It is more economical, but often disadvantageous, to prohibit clarifications.

There is a distinction to be made between clarification and modification of proposals. In American commercial practice, clarifications are permissible. On the other hand, modification of proposals after submittal may be considered unfair. In many parts of the world, modification of proposals is considered part of the bargaining process, a method of getting the best possible price. Bidders may be requested to go through several rounds of modifications. This process may be satisfactory if the procedure is understood by all parties ahead of time. If this is the practice, allowances must be made in the person-day budget and the schedule. In such situations also, the specification will be subject to attack by bidders trying to reduce their cost. The engineer will have to be able to defend the requirements. Indefensible requirements will lead to extra expenditure of evaluation time as proposal modifications are made and evaluated.

The final product of the technical review is a technical recommendation. It should state that certain bidders have satisfactory proposals. Cost adjustments may be proposed for inclusion in the economic evaluation.

Conducting an Economic Evaluation for a Fixed-Price Contract

Discussion of an economic evaluation in this book assumes that this matter is assigned to the technical department. However, the purchasing department might conduct the economic evaluation.

Conducting an economic evaluation can be very simple. If the specification is part of a fixed-price contract with a short delivery time and a single payment, the lowest price is obviously the right one to accept. If matters are so simple, the engineer will scarcely be involved.

The basic complication in an economic analysis is the time value of money. The later a payment can be made, the more favorable it is for the buyer.

The mathematical model commonly applied in economic evaluations is called the *present-worth method*. It is based on the premise that money needed for a payment in the future can be invested until needed. Today's money can accumulate interest until needed. Therefore, the amount of money which must be set aside today is less than that needed at the time of payment. The sum which must be set aside today is the present worth of the future payment.

The present-worth method is only a tool for evaluation. The present-worth amount will probably not be actually set aside and invested, since companies have many alternatives for employing their money. Such matters are of no concern to the evaluator, since his or her responsibility is restricted to the evaluation at hand. What the evaluator does need to know is the interest rate to be used in the calculations. This number should be supplied by the buyer's financial personnel and should represent the cost of money to the buyer.

Let us assume two proposals are available, differing only in their payment schedules. The present worth of each payment can be calculated and summed for each bidder. The lesser sum is the lower evaluated price. For a simple case such as this, a compound interest table such as found in Ref. 1 can be used in the calculation. For more complex cases, the methods presented in an engineering economics book such as Ref. 2 can be used.

The simple method described above does not take inflation into account. If appreciable inflation is expected during the payment period, most vendors will insist on an adjustment. The evaluator has to estimate this adjustment to the payments and increase the present worth accordingly.

Similarly, in international commerce, an adjustment may need to be made for estimated changes in currency exchange rates. This is a very speculative matter, but, at a minimum, the risk of dealing in foreign currencies must be acknowledged.

Since the purpose of the economic analysis is to select a vendor, it should be kept as simple as that goal will permit. If a fixed price is the only consideration, the present-worth model as described above will suffice to arrange the bids in order of increasing evaluated price.

If both the initial and operating costs are to be evaluated, a more elaborate economic model must be used. Conceptually, the method usually used is to reduce costs to an equivalent periodic (monthly or annual) payment.

Operating cost might vary for equipment offered by different bidders. For example, one motor might be more efficient than another, resulting in a lower electricity cost. Also, superior materials may be judged to result in lower maintenance cost.

Once the operating costs are estimated, it is easy to place them in the periodic payment format. The capital cost is more difficult. The usual method is to use a concept known as the capital recovery factor. The *capital recovery factor* is based on the idea that a periodic payment into a fund can be made such that, at the end of the life of the equipment, enough money has been accumulated in the fund to recover the capital originally invested in the equipment. While money is in the fund, it accumulates interest. The amount of the annual payment can be easily calculated if the interest rate and service life of the equipment can be estimated.

A further complication in estimating cost is taxes. Some taxes are proportional to the value of equipment. The value is based on the initial cost of the equipment and an annual decrease determined by rules in the tax law. The annual equivalent tax payment can be determined by setting up a fund similar to the capital recovery fund.

The sum of the annual payments for operating cost, capital recovery, and taxes represents the total cost of the equipment. It can be used for evaluation of the proposals. Again, more information on economic analysis methods can be found in Ref. 2.

Conducting an Economic Evaluation for a Cost-Type Contract

Cost-plus and time and materials contracts also require a technical and an economic evaluation. Because these contract arrangements are used in less determinant situations, a more subjective approach is required for evaluation. Specification compliance and numerical evaluation of cost are not applicable.

As with fixed-price specifications, the first step in evaluation is establishment of a bidders list. This screening step can be formalized by sending a spectrum of potential bidders a request for a statement of qualifications. This document should be structured to elicit a brief response customized to fit the project in prospect. It is unfair to expect an extensive response, since the request is sent to a large number of potential bidders, only one of which will be ultimately successful. From the perspective of the respondents, the probability of success is small. An intelligent organization will not be inclined to spend much money replying to a request for qualifications.

The specification must be written to elicit the information needed to perform the evaluation. In a cost-type project, the technical evaluation is based on the strength of the bidder, that is, the bidder's personnel, experience, past performance, and facilities, rather than on the features of the bidder's product. The features of the product will be developed as the project progresses. Therefore, the information requests contained in the specification will ask more questions about the bidder's ability than about the proposed product. Text, rather than fill-in sheets, are commonly used for the information requests, since the replies are expected to be too extensive to fit on fill-in sheets.

The technical evaluation will then be performed by using evaluation criteria as described in Chap. 8 and the information presented in the proposals.

The economic evaluation of a cost-type contract can often be a simple matter of computing the average cost of a person-day. The economic evaluation is not as important as in a fixed-price contract, since an organization that is highly rated on a technical basis will probably take less person-days to complete the project than a lower-rated one. Also, the actions of a competent organization can have consequences beyond their own cost. A good architectural organization, for example, can produce a more economical and functional design than a less competent one would.

Preparing the Evaluation Report

This subject has been treated from the manager's point of view in Chap. 4. A suggested outline for the report was presented in Table 4-1.

The engineer's duty is to produce an adequate report with a minimum of person-days. The engineer therefore wants to keep it simple and short. This goal must be compromised by producing a report that convinces the client that the right conclusion has been reached, and perhaps one that leaves an adequate record of why the successful bidder was chosen. The record may be necessary to prove that the engineer's duty was performed in a responsible manner. The client may also need to keep the justification on file to reply to later criticism, especially if the client is a public body or a regulated utility subject to outside review.

Since an evaluation report is a report, its format and language are governed by report practices, rather than specification practices. An evaluation report should be composed so that a casual reader can determine the sense of the report from a summary. It should be assumed that a reader with a more detailed interest will read the entire report.

References

1. Eugene Avallone and Theodore Baumeister III (eds.) *Marks' Standard Handbook for Mechanical Engineers,* 9th ed., McGraw-Hill Book Company, New York, 1987.

2. James L. Riggs, *Engineering Economics,* 2d ed., McGraw-Hill Book Company, New York, 1982.

12
Enforcement Techniques

General

A specification must be written so that it can be enforced. The primary goal of specification writing is to be so clear that no disputes arise and the goods are delivered as the specifier intended. Failing this ideal, the next best is that all differences are resolved by the vendor and the specifier with no outside assistance or interference and the goods are delivered on time and without an increase in price. The ultimate worst alternative is that the goods are never delivered and the two parties appear in court.

If a contract is fixed price, the usual intent is that the goods will be delivered in accordance with the contract, without further modification. If a contract is on a cost basis, the usual intent is that changes will be made as the project progresses. The contract must have a mechanism for making these changes, such as a change clause, which is used to redirect the vendor in an orderly manner as the project progresses. The change clause should document each change in a contract and the costs associated with it. Enforcement of a cost-type contract is more difficult than that of a fixed-price contract, since the ability to cite specific requirements is not necessarily present. Control over a cost-type contract can be lost if one does not use the change procedure religiously.

It is important to start a procurement action with a clear contract. The parties must understand what documents—the specification, the proposal, or some other document—govern. It is especially necessary that the technical people who interact on a daily basis understand. If they do not understand their rights and obligations, disputes will inevitably arise. This means that the specification enforcement engineers must know not only what the specification says, but also what the purchasing department agreed to in negotiating the contract.

As one writes a specification, three basic factors which govern specification enforcement should continuously be kept in mind.

Clarity. The vendor cannot comply with requirements if they are not understandable.

Reasonability. Vendors are disposed to ignore requirements they do not consider reasonable. Sometimes the vendor needs to be educated. For example, early in the nuclear industry, some vendors considered seismic requirements a joke. It was only after much careful explanation that they complied.

Verifiability. The vendor and the purchaser must be able to agree, beyond a reasonable doubt, that the requirements have or have not been met. This implies that the requirements must be explicit and verifiable. For example, it is better to state "the motor shall be sized to drive the fan at rated flow and head without exceeding its nameplate rating" than to state "the motor shall be adequately sized to drive the load." It is best if the requirements can be verified by inspecting the goods. If this is not possible, other means as described below may be used.

Writing for enforcement can be overdone. If a writer is overly concerned with enforcing the specification in every detail, the writer may specify inspections and data submittals which have unnecessarily high costs.

The Proposal

The proposal is the bidder's reply to a specification. If a provision in it contradicts the specification, the purchaser has to decide whether to accept the exception, request the bidder to modify the proposal, or reject the proposal. If the purchaser is silent, the bidder, when designated as the vendor, may properly insist on delivering the goods in accordance with the proposal, rather than the specification. Therefore, the proposal should be thoroughly reviewed.

The specification should require that bidders include information in their proposals which covers the important aspects of the specification. The information requested should be sufficient to demonstrate that the bidders understand what they are to provide. Techniques for eliciting information, such as fill-in sheets, have been described in earlier chapters.

Document Submittal

Most specifications require submittal of documents after the contract is signed. Such documents serve three purposes:

1. They provide information the design professional needs to perform his or her work.
2. They provide information other parties need to perform their work. Examples are the contractor, who needs erection information, and the owner, who needs maintenance and operating information.
3. They prove that the vendor understands the specification and will deliver goods in accordance with it.

Most of the documents submitted will be drawings. They are sometimes referred to collectively as *vendor drawings* or, in the building industry, as *shop drawings*. Submittals will include other documents, for example, operating and maintenance instructions.

One must put the proper words in the specification to require the necessary submittals. The procedures for processing the submittals are covered in Chap. 6.

The rights-obligation syndrome was discussed in Chap. 6. Briefly put, the law believes that if one has a right, that person also has the corresponding obligation. In this case, if one has the right to use document submittal as a means of enforcing the specification, that person has the obligation to do so. If a vendor submits a document for approval showing features that are not in accordance with the specification, that vendor has a right to expect that the noncompliance will be detected. Later detection of the noncompliance, for instance upon installation, will result in a dispute which the owner is likely to lose. It may be too late to make a change, and the vendor will use the approval to argue that no money need be returned. Most design professionals try to avoid this problem by claiming that their approval is not for enforcement, and their approval or review stamp displays this position. This claim is really an evasion, since the owner usually expects the design professional to detect noncompliance. If the record in fact shows that the design professional did actually use approval as an enforcement mechanism, his or her disclaimers will probably not prevail.

Asking for too much information increases work and cost. Information requests should therefore have a serious purpose. They should not be used to satisfy idle curiosity. Asking for too little information may result in receiving unsuitable goods and perhaps in some people not being able to do their jobs. One must have foresight and competence to strike the right balance.

A specification should clearly state what information is to be submitted. This subject is important enough to deserve a separate section. In this section, the drawings or documents should be specified by title. The action to be taken by the buyer (e.g., approval or retention for information) should be stated. This section should be tabular in form. Requirements for contents of the documents can be placed in the Technical Requirements section, or they can follow the tabulation. The former is the usual practice. It puts the document requirements in a place where they are most likely to be seen by the technical people who must create the documents. The latter concentrates document requirements in one place, where they may be better comprehended by the management.

Approval rights (see Chap. 6) need to be stated somewhere in the procurement document. They are often in the Commercial section, since they are standard for the project and often viewed as a quasi-legal matter. Many vendors are sensitive about permitting broad approval rights, so negotiations on this point may be required.

Ideally, the purpose of document approval should also be stated. The principle that approval will not be used to change specification requirements may have to be stated, since many vendors are sensitive on this point. Use of approval to ensure that engineers and others get the information necessary to do their work should also be stated. Any mention that drawings and documents will be inspected for specification compliance should probably be avoided unless industry practices require it. For example, in some industries detailed structural drawings must be reviewed to assure that the designer's concept was carried out properly. If such is the industry practice and therefore the design professional's obligation, it is only fair to acknowledge it.

It is also necessary to specify a schedule for the submittal of information and to hold the vendor to it. Vendors may delay submittals in the hope of evading requirements. Presumably, the engineer has a schedule to meet and needs the information on time to do so. On the other hand, the engineer has an obligation to approve the document on schedule. The engineer cannot expect the vendor to perform on schedule if he or she will not.

The use of document submittals to enforce specification requirements has the advantage that it occurs early in the production cycle, before schedule pressure mounts and major commitments of material are made. It is easier for the vendor to repair mistakes than it would be later.

It is unfair, and bad practice, to use drawing approval to change specification requirements. Unilateral changes only cause disputes and acrimony. If a specification change is required, the request should be made by mutual agreement between the parties. The formal change can be made by an addendum to the contract or by a less formal, but mutually agreeable procedure, such as an exchange of letters. A price change may be necessary.

It is also important to use document submittals as specified. If design professionals are not making adequate comments on document submittals, it may indicate that approvals are overspecified, thus wasting everybody's time and money. Requests for changes after a drawing has been approved are an invitation to cost additions and disruptive to the schedule. The vendor has a right to adequate action on submittals.

Inspection

Inspection rights must be established in the specification and accepted before a contract is signed. It is very difficult to establish inspection rights later because the vendor has little interest in granting them, even for additional money. Inspection is a threat to the vendor. It has the potential for costing much money if the inspections find fault or even if they delay production without finding fault. It is difficult to charge an amount of extra charges commensurate with the perceived threat.

The most reliable form of inspection is that performed by the owner's representative. Since the representative is an employee of the owner, he or she has the owner's interest at heart. If inspection by the owner's representative is desired, that right must be clearly established in the specification. The scheduling of the inspection must also be included. The schedule must be defined in terms of a step in the vendor's production schedule, rather than date, since the vendor needs flexibility to perform the work. These steps are called *hold points*. At a hold point, the vendor's obligation is to hold production for a specified period of time so that the inspector can get to the vendor's shop and perform the inspection. If the inspector is late, the vendor has the right to proceed.

An example of a hold point is after reinforcing bar is in position but prior to placing concrete. Placing concrete will make the reinforcing bar invisible and thus prohibit inspection. The specification should require that the owner be informed that a hold point will be reached about 2 days before the event is expected to occur. This time is, in most cases, long enough for the inspector to respond, but short enough that production will not be overly delayed or the inspector's time wasted if progress is miscalculated. The specification should also state what facilities are to be provided by the vendor to assist the inspector.

One common buyer's inspection is the shipping inspection. This occurs when the goods have been finished and are ready for shipment. It has the advantage that the goods are complete. The inspector can review the specification completely against the goods in their completed state. It has the disadvantage that some features, internal to the equipment, are concealed by assembly. Also, performance data is not necessarily available. This inspection occurs late in the procurement cycle, so the buyer may be under schedule pressure to accept the equipment. On the other hand, the vendor often does not receive payment until the equipment is shipped. The vendor is therefore under financial pressure to pass the shipping inspection.

Equipment is also often inspected by the buyer upon receipt. This inspection need not be mentioned in the specification, since no action on the vendor's part is required. It is also difficult to obtain corrective action from the vendor since, at a minimum, the goods must be shipped back to the vendor. It is easier to obtain corrections from the vendor if the vendor has not been paid.

An alternate to inspection by the owner is inspection by the vendor with appropriate submittal of documents. The inspection is less reliable, since vendors have been known to submit false information. If the vendor has a good reputation, this procedure is advantageous since vendor inspection is generally more economical than buyer inspection. If vendor inspection is specified, one must be careful to do so completely. The author once had a case where a vendor said the test would be performed, but would not share the results with the buyer, since that was not specified. One must be careful to specify what tests are to be run, what procedures are to be used, what criteria are used to evaluate the test, whether witnessing by the buyer is necessary, and what shall be done with the results. Sometimes the results are submitted to the owner. Sometimes they are retained at the vendor's facility for review during visits by the buyer's representative. If the test is to be witnessed by the buyer's representative, criteria for scheduling the test and notifying the buyer must be in the specification.

Inspection by third parties can also be specified, directly or indirectly. For example, if it is specified that equipment must be in accordance with the ASME Boiler and Pressure Vessel Code, the ASME inspector will certify compliance with the code. Similarly, the American Bureau of Shipping will inspect marine equipment. Such inspections are reliable and complete.

Other Enforcement Techniques

It is difficult to enforce a specification with frivolous requirements. If a vendor questions requirements and is told it is not necessary to adhere to them, the vendor will soon assume that any inconvenient requirements need not be adhered to. Every time a buyer backs down on a requirement, it becomes more difficult to enforce the next requirement. To improve enforceability, a completed specification should be reviewed and any superfluous requirements deleted.

On the other hand, enforcement is enhanced if the vendor perceives requirements as reasonable. Vendor engineers are professional people and get a sense of accomplishment from good products. If the specification appears to be directed toward that goal, they will cooperate to the best of their ability.

The buyer's reputation can improve enforcement. If a specification is reasonable and the vendor knows that the buyer will insist on its provisions, the vendor is less likely to engage in a fruitless effort to evade the specification. It takes time to develop a reputation. It is gained by consistent behavior, specification after specification. One should endeavor to enforce specifications fairly and consistently. This endeavor will become easier as time goes on and the vendors learn what to expect.

Enforcement action should be taken as soon as the deviation is detected. Prompt action impresses the vendor. Also, the earlier in the production cycle a change is made, the easier it is for the vendor.

The most effective method of enforcing a specification is by a letter stating what section of the specification was violated and what the deviation was, and asking for specific corrective action. As a courtesy, such a letter should be preceded by a telephone call. If the specification is clear and reasonable, and the letter is prompt, it will usually get the desired result.

Summary

Table 12-1 shows an analysis of enforcement provisions in a typical specification. To assist in review of specifications, Table 12-2 presents a checklist for enforcement provisions.

Table 12-1. Example of Specification Enforcement Provisions
Imaginary Project 1: Centrifugal Pumps Specification

Provision	Means of enforcement
Rated head and flow	Test witnessed by engineer. Specification requires test be conducted, engineer permitted to witness, notice of test given
Motor adequately sized	Review of motor data. Specification requires submittal
Pump fits in space allotted	Review of arrangement drawing. Specification requires submittal and allotts space
Motor has Underwriters' Laboratory seal	Receiving inspection
Shaft coupling of specified design	Shipping inspection. Specification requires notification of shipping date, access for inspector
Impeller material specified	Review of material list. Specification requires submittal. Receiving inspection

Table 12-2. Enforcement Checklist

1. Clarity
   a. Will the vendor understand the requirements?
   b. Are the requirements organized so that they can be easily found?
2. Reasonability
   a. Are there any superfluous requirements?
   b. Are all requirements directly related to obtaining satisfactory goods?
3. Verifiability
   a. Are all requirements specific?
   b. If verification is by document submittal, has submittal of the necessary documents been specified?
   c. If verification is by test,
      (1) Have test procedures been specified?
      (2) Have success and failure criteria been specified?
      (3) Will test results be submitted or has provision been made for engineer witnessing?
   d. If verification is by inspection,
      (1) Have inspector's rights been specified?
      (2) Have the inspections been scheduled?
      (3) Alternatively, have hold points been specified, with provision for notifying the inspector?

13
Production

The Writer's Task—Outline

This section is intended to guide the writer through specification preparation. Table 13-1 shows the steps involved.

Accept the Assignment

Let us assume that your supervisor has assigned you to write a specification. The first thing you must do is to determine whether you can

Table 13-1. Steps in Writing a Specification

1. Accept the assignment
   Budget
   Schedule
   Technical ability

2. Define the project
   Scope
   Specification type
   Format
   Bidding procedures
   Evaluation procedures

3. Gather information
   Design parameters
   Features

4. Choose a writing technique

5. Prepare an outline

6. Write

7. Check

8. Secure approvals

9. Coordinate with word processing

meet your supervisor's expectations. You must determine what they are, most importantly, schedule, budget, and product characteristics. If you conclude that you cannot meet the expectations, it is incumbent on you to speak up promptly and to be able to defend your case. Success will depend not only on the strength of the case at hand but on the reputation you have previously established. At this time, it may be possible to adjust the schedule and budget or to shift the assignment to somebody better qualified, without hurting the project. Later, adjustments may not be so easy.

One must be careful in complaining about schedule and budget. It is a manager's duty to be a good judge of both. If one complains, he or she must be able to explain rationally why the schedule and budget are not feasible. Absent a good explanation, management is justifiably inclined to think their judgment correct and yours, therefore, wrong.

At this stage, the writer must have a preliminary idea of all the processes he or she will go through in writing the specification. Initially, the most important item to be understood is the scope, in other words, what the specification is about. If the specification concerns a subject familiar to the writer, it is obviously less work than if it is not. It is also easier to judge how much time it will take to write the specification.

If the schedule and budget are acceptable to the writer, he or she can proceed to the next step.

Define the Problem

The next step is to define the problem in greater detail. This process can be described as developing a plan for writing the specification. It is now time to establish the following parameters at a minimum:

Scope. A preliminary draft of the scope section should be prepared.

Type of specification. Commodity, catalog, or full specification.

Format restrictions. Strict format requirements may increase the labor required. Also, such restrictions may make it difficult to adapt previous specifications.

Bidding procedures. If the bidders are restricted, a simpler specification will suffice.

Evaluation procedures. These procedures influence the amount of information that bidders are requested to provide in their proposals. Also, if the vendor can be selected on the basis of perceived value, a less restrictive specification need be written than if price and adherence to the specification will be the only evaluation criteria.

Gather Information

This subject was covered extensively in Chap. 2. At this stage of writing a specification, it is short-term information that is required. This information can be divided into the following categories:

Design parameters

Features

Quality requirements

Codes and standards

Choose a Writing Technique

Writing techniques will be discussed in the next section. The simplest one is to copy a previous specification. Even if technically feasible, format requirements may make this technique impractical. The most difficult technique is original writing.

Prepare an Outline

The outline intended here is a writing tool. It need not follow any of the rules taught in school if they get in the way of planning the work. It should follow, at least generally, the format dictated by project requirements.

The first step in preparing an outline is to list the subjects that should be covered in the specification in random order as they come to mind. The goal here is to capture all the subjects. Once on paper, they can be arranged in the order and grouped into sections as dictated by the project format. Once arranged, they can be refined into an outline.

Writing

Writing is work. With the outline at hand and the writing technique selected, writing is simply a process of pushing along until the work is done.

Checking

The writer usually checks his or her work twice—before and after typing. The first check is to see that the draft is legible and suitable for release. The goal is to ensure that the word processing group can type the specification successfully and, preferably, only once. The second check is to see that the word processing group satisfactorily interpreted the specification. The checks are not proofreading. That is a mechanical process performed by the word processing group as part of its quality control.

The writer also needs to check that all the quantities and design parameters are correct and current, that all project requirements have been met, and that the specification is technically sound. To the best of the writer's ability, the specification should be ready to be released to bidders at this time. Ideally, management should find no flaws.

Secure Approvals

Using the proactive philosophy, it is the writer's duty to secure approval of his or her work. It is part of meeting the schedule. If the work was done right the first time, securing approval should be easy.

Coordinate with Word Processing

This is also a part of meeting the schedule. The writer must ensure that word processing has no undue difficulty interpreting the specification.

Writing Techniques

Pen and Paper

Setting pen to paper appears to be a tedious process, but actually, speed in writing something as meticulous as an original specification is limited by the rate of thinking rather than that of writing. For most engineers, the mechanics of writing by pen are performed by an automatic process which does not interfere with creative thought. Typing, which is learned at a later age, usually requires a less automatic thought process which does interfere. Even for a typist of some skill, therefore, original writing may be quicker by pen. This general statement needs to be applied with common sense. Perhaps the best rule for a supervisor to follow is to let engineers use whatever technique they feel will be most productive. Many engineers will choose pen and paper. If one prefers a computer, it will be cost-effective to let him or her use one.

Writing by pen does have the disadvantage that someone eventually will have to convert the manuscript into a computer file. Although laborious and time-consuming, this is not a particularly expensive process. However, time must be allowed for it in the schedule.

Another perennial problem with manuscripts is legibility. The author has an obligation to produce a text which can be read by the typist. Some specification writers have poor handwriting. Supervisors must insist on legibility but must also resist draconian and counterproductive methods of getting it, like insisting that everything be printed. Cost is usually on the side of requiring the minimum practical from the writer.

The writer also has an obligation to produce copy that is in accordance with project standards. Editing a writer's product should be unnecessary. Editing by a lay person or a professional unfamiliar with the technology of a specification can be dangerous, since he or she can distort the meaning of a specification without intending to.

The language in a specification is deliberately simple and direct. If a specification writer's thoughts are clear, he or she should have no difficulty expressing them in specification terms.

In an effort to reduce the writer's time, the writer should be expected to furnish only the text of a specification. The word processing group can add peripheral items such as the table of contents and the title page.

A writer should be expected to write about 4 to 6 pages of manuscript a day. This rule is based on an original specification with all the performance parameters available. It also assumes a mature engineer with a knowledge of the technology in the specification. It allows some time for investigation into codes and standards to be applied and into the availability of products.

Copying

The easiest and most economical way to write a specification is to copy an existing one. An experienced, well-organized technical group will have standard specifications or specifications from previous projects to copy from.

If practical, one should talk to the author of the source specification to find out whether there were any problems with it. There is no point in perpetuating mistakes.

It is seldom that a source specification will be completely applicable. More commonly, a certain amount of updating will be required. If the source specification is available as a computer file, it can be easily changed, and the word-entry step can be omitted.

One must be wary of legal problems in copying specifications. The source specification may be copyrighted. Even if not formally copyrighted, it may still be someone else's property. It may be protected by a common law copyright, if it was not in the public domain.

In specification writing, there is no stigma attached to copying. A specification writer does not prize originality for its own sake but takes pride in results; a project well executed.

Cut and Paste

It is most probable that a specification will be an amalgam of new and old. The classical method of producing such a specification is called cut and paste, although paste is obsolete. Staples and transparent tape are much handier.

Copying machines are also an important tool for this technique.

The starting point for a cut-and-paste product is a copy of the source specification, which is used with interspersed corrections as far as possible. When a block of inappropriate material for the new specification is found, or it is desired to add in different text, the source specification is cut off and a handwritten section spliced in, using staples or transparent tape. Sections of source specification and manuscript can be alternated until the specification is finished.

As described above, the product of the cut-and-paste method is hard copy which must be entered into the computer system. Although the system is convenient to the writer, it creates work for the word processing group.

A much better method of combining specifications is what might be called electronic cut and paste. The starting point is a computer file version of the source specification in word processing format. The word processing program must be one the engineer is versatile in. The engineer then uses the word processing program to correct, delete, or add text. Some writers, especially the younger ones, are adept enough at word processing to create specifications this way. Their willingness and ability depends on how much new text must be created. The product is a computer file which can be easily manipulated, stored, and reproduced. The tedious step of word processing is skipped.

A well-developed organization will have a computer file of source specifications. This file should be protected from modification by unauthorized personnel. The safest way to protect the reference file is to place it on an isolated computer system under the word processing group's control. Writers should be allowed to obtain data from the reference file only by hard copy or floppy disk. If this protection scheme is judged too inconvenient, access to the reference file can be restricted by password.

General

The specification writer is responsible for delivery of the entire specification text including written sections, data sheets, and drawings.

Data sheets should be on printed forms. Data filled in by hand is perfectly acceptable, provided it is legible.

Drawings are an excellent medium for transmitting graphical information. They are preferred over text for this purpose. It is inefficient to use drawings for text or tabulations. Even if computer techniques are used, a drawing program is a poor substitute for a word processing program. However, communication will be clearer if industry norms are respected. In the building industry, schedules showing quantities are often placed on drawings.

Word Processing

The use of computers for word processing is now almost universal. Simple typewriters are obsolete because a specification modification results in laborious retyping. Text can be much more easily manipulated with a computer and word processing software.

A large, well-established specification writing organization will probably use some form of mainframe-based word processing system, administered by a centralized word processing group. Such a system will permit several large projects to be served simultaneously and a large number of standard specifications to be stored. Communication with such a computer system must be formal because there is a large amount of data to be kept organized, and there is a danger that unauthorized people may corrupt the database.

A smaller organization will probably use personal computers linked by a local area network. Such systems are inexpensive and effective.

Methods for planning the use of workers in a specification effort were described in Chap. 1. A specification list and schedule as described there can be used for planning word processing hardware as well. A large project might need 200 specifications. Each specification might contain 50 pages on the average. The total text might then amount to 10,000 pages. The text could be contained on a single 60 megabyte hard disk, assuming that only the current edition of each specification is saved. If a computer system dedicated to specification writing on this project is desired, it could consist of five networked personal computers. One, containing the hard disk, should be based on an 80386 chip, or one of equivalent power. The others could be based on an 8088 or similar chip, since word processing does not require much computer power. In selecting the model of computer to be used, do not forget that 8088 chip machines can read only to or from double-density floppy disks. 80286-based machines can read both double-density or high-density disks. The choice of machine must be compatible with the medium the organization's data is stored on. Each of the computers should be equipped with two floppy disk drives. Backup should be provided by tape or a Bernouli box to avoid losing data due to a hard disk crash.

The above description applies only if IBM-compatible machines are used. Apple-compatible machines could also be applied.

These computers should be connected by a local area network. The project data base should reside on the hard disk. Specifications can be down loaded to one of the other computers for processing. Any one of the computers can also transfer a specification to a floppy disk if an engineer wants to put it on his or her own computer for modification. Floppy disks can also be used to put text from other sources into the system, perhaps for use in specifications. Completed specifications can be transferred to the hard disk for storage.

The computer system should also contain a printer connected to the network so that it can be accessed from any computer. It should be of at least near-letter quality, since its product will be sent to the client and to vendors.

The word processing group should be headed by a competent, well-organized, level-headed person with a helpful attitude. An engineer is not necessary. Indeed it is better that this leader not be an engineer since such a person might be tempted to disrupt production by improving the product. The word processing leader will need an understanding of word processing programs and the application of personal computer equipment. He or she will need the ability to organize the work and assign personnel so that all work is finished on time. It is an unfortunate human tendency to put off completing a specification manuscript until the last minute, leaving the word processing group insufficient time to perform their work properly. Engineers will often produce conflict situations this way, which must be mediated by the word processing supervisor.

The members of the word processing group need to be good typists with a knowledge of computer word processing. The word processing group transforms the specification manuscript into a form suitable for transmission to the client and bidders. This process includes typing and assembly of ancillary materials such as drawing and data sheets. They also save copies of all specifications on the hard disk. They will be needed for future reference and also as a starting point for any revisions of the specification.

A record copy of each edition of the specification sent out of house should be retained. This copy should not be in the computer system since there it is susceptible to corruption through modification. It can be a hard copy, on microfiche, or on an optical disk, whichever fits the needs of the organization best. The word processing group will also see that sufficient hard copies of the specification are available for the bidders and for use inside the organization. The actual work of reproduction is done elsewhere.

Index

About the Author

David C. Purdy is Vice President of Engineering for Applied Power Associates, Inc., in Omaha, Nebraska. He has over 38 years of experience in various mechanical engineering–project management positions and has worked as Chief Proposal Engineer for Gibbs and Hill, Inc. in New York, and as a project engineer for Babcock and Wilcox in Lynchburg, Virginia. The holder of several patents and the author of numerous engineering articles, David Purdy holds a B.S. degree in Marine Engineering and Naval Architecture from the Webb Institute. He is a member of the American Society of Mechanical Engineers and a registered professional engineer in Virginia, New York, and Nebraska. David Purdy is a resident of Omaha, Nebraska.